EFT FOR PTSD
(POST-TRAUMATIC STRESS DISORDER)

Judy Depenau
246 Benton St
Santa Rosa CA
95401

by Gary Craig

www.EFTUniverse.com

Energy Psychology Press
P.O. Box 442
Fulton, CA 95439
www.energypsychologypress.com

Cataloging-in-Publication Data

Craig, Gary, 1940–
EFT for PTSD / Gary Craig. — 1st ed.
    p. cm.
Includes bibliographical references and index.
ISBN 978-1-60415-040-7
1. Post-traumatic stress disorder—Treatment. I. Title.
RC552.P67C73 2008
616.85'2106—dc22

2008046923

This book demonstrates an impressive personal improvement tool. It
is not a substitute for training in psychology or psychotherapy. Nothing contained herein is meant to replace qualified medical advice. The
author urges the reader to use these techniques under the supervision of a
qualified therapist or physician. The author and publisher do not assume
responsibility for how the reader chooses to apply the techniques herein.

Cover design by Victoria Valentine
Editing by CJ Puotinen
Typesetting by Karin Kinsey
Typeset in Cochin and Adobe Garamond
Printed in USA by Bang Printing
First Edition

10 9 8 7 6 5 4 3 2 1

Important note: While EFT has produced remarkable clinical results, it must still be considered to be in the experimental stage and thus practitioners and the public must take complete responsibility for their use of it. Further, Gary Craig is not a licensed health professional and offers EFT as an ordained minister and as a personal performance coach.

This book is written for psychologists, psychiatrists, social workers, health care professionals, counselors, and others who work with patients who suffer from Post-Traumatic Stress Disorder as well as for those who have PTSD.

If you suffer from PTSD yourself, please consult a qualified health practitioner regarding your use of EFT. Then read the entire book, paying special attention to Chapter Thirteen. EFT can be a valuable tool for those motivated to help themselves, but for Post-Traumatic Stress Disorder, it should be used with specific safeguards that are explained in Chapter Thirteen.

Contents

Acknowledgments

The list of individuals who contributed to the development of EFT can never be complete because most of them lived over 5,000 years ago. Those are the brilliant physicians who discovered and mapped the centerpiece of EFT, namely, the subtle energies that course through our bodies. These subtle energies are also the centerpiece of acupuncture and, as a result, EFT and acupuncture are cousins. Both disciplines are growing rapidly here in the West and, as time unfolds, they are destined to have a primary role in emotional and physical healing.

In the 20th Century, other dedicated souls advanced our use of ancient techniques that utilize the body's energy. Principal among them is Dr. George Goodheart, who developed Applied Kinesiology, a forerunner of EFT. In the 1960s, Dr. Goodheart discovered that muscle testing could be used to gather important information from the body, and he went on to train many health care practitioners and publish important books and papers.

Dr. John Diamond's work deserves applause because, to my knowledge, he was one of the first psychiatrists to use and write about these subtle energies. His many pioneering concepts, together with advanced ideas from Applied Kinesiology, have formed the foundation upon which our work is constructed. Dr. Diamond's best-sellers include *Life Energy: Using the Meridians to Unlock the Power of Your Emotions* (Continuum International, 1990) and *Life Energy and the Emotions* (Eden Grove, 1997).

Dr. Roger Callahan, the clinical psychologist from whom I received my original introduction to "emotional acupressure," deserves all the credit history can give him. He was the first to bring these techniques to the public in a substantial way and he did so despite open hostility from his own profession. As you might appreciate, it takes heavy doses of conviction to plow through the ingrained beliefs of conventional thinking.

Without Roger Callahan's missionary drive, we might still be sitting around theorizing about this "interesting thing."

It is upon the shoulders of these giants that I humbly stand. My own contribution to the rapidly expanding field of meridian therapies has been to reduce the unnecessary complexity that inevitably finds its way into new discoveries. EFT is an elegantly simple version of these procedures, which professionals and laypeople alike can use on a variety of problems.

I also owe a special debt of gratitude to Adrienne Fowlie, who, through a friend, introduced me to meridian tapping techniques and helped me develop EFT.

Many EFT students and practitioners helped make this book possible. I am grateful to all who contributed case studies and reports. Many of the examples given here were published in our email newsletter and are posted in the newsletter's archives on the EFT website, www.EFTUniverse.com.

The names given in the reports presented here have often been changed to protect the privacy of those involved. This is especially likely if only first names are given. All of the names given here are as they originally appeared in reports published in our newsletter and on the EFT website. When a person's full name is given, it has not been changed and is used with permission.

In the interests of editorial consistency, reports from the United Kingdom, Australia, Canada, and other countries that use British spelling and punctuation have been changed to conform to standard American English.

Many references are made to the V.A., which stands for hospitals and services run by the United States Department of Veterans Affairs, especially its Veterans Benefits Administration and Veterans Health Administration.

Like most topics of special interest, EFT has its own words and abbreviations that have special meaning for its students and practitioners. You'll find a list of EFT terms and their definitions in the Glossary at the end of this book.

Gary Craig

Introduction

Emotional Freedom Techniques, or EFT, is a do-it-yourself procedure that has helped people of all ages deal with many different kinds of problems and conditions, including problems associated with traumatic memories.

EFT combines acupressure (gentle fingertip tapping on key acupuncture points) with focused thought. In other words, you tap on a few points, mostly on the head and torso, while you think about a problem.

How something so simple can work so quickly and effectively remains a mystery, but it's one that researchers are working to solve. In the mean time, studies confirm that EFT can help those with Post-Traumatic Stress Disorder in record time with lasting results.

My main reason for writing this book is to give instruction on a method that will help our veterans and others who suffer from Post-Traumatic Stress Disorder in a way that nothing else has.

I wrote this book so that mental health professionals and trauma specialists around the world can learn about EFT and some of the research that proves its effectiveness in the treatment of PTSD.

I wrote it for the United States Department of Veterans Affairs, formerly called the Veterans Administration, because by adopting EFT, V.A. medical centers can alleviate military PTSD in record time.

I wrote this book for the public. Post-Traumatic Stress Disorder is much in the news, and almost all of us have at least a few symptoms, major or minor. Knowing how to use EFT to help ourselves and others is a precious gift.

I wrote this book so that veterans themselves can use it, and so can police, fire fighters, medical workers, and others whose careers involve stress and trauma, as well as for their spouses and families.

Ideally, veterans and others with PTSD will use EFT as homework between sessions with a professional therapist, but if veterans do not want to work with, cannot afford, or do not trust professionals, they can use it on their own. If this is your situation, please read the entire book and then study Chapter Thirteen before trying EFT.

In 1994, I spent six days with Vietnam War veterans living in a Los Angeles Veterans Administration Hospital. The sessions, which were videotaped, involved patients who could not sleep through the night, whose lives were haunted by vivid intrusive memories, and who suffered from mood swings, tremors, paranoid thoughts, and high anxiety. All of them had undergone conventional psychotherapy, some for as long as 20 or 30 years, but neither the therapy nor the psychoactive prescription drugs they took freed them from the extreme emotional pain that their memories generated. Not only did EFT accomplish that goal, but when the veterans tried it on their own, it worked just as well as when my colleague and I guided their sessions. That was the beginning of my deep appreciation for EFT's powerful effects on old or stored emotional traumas.

More recently, in March of 2008, I worked with five other EFT practitioners and coaches in a research study involving nine veterans and two of their family members, all of whom suffered from PTSD or related issues. This five-day conference, which was filmed for a forthcoming movie and which was documented with psychological tests, produced equally impressive results.

Throughout EFT's short history, we have received numerous reports from practitioners and beginners alike describing how a few sessions of EFT tapping reduced and then eliminated PTSD stemming from war experiences, terrorist attacks, accidents, injuries, emotional abuse, physical violence, and other damaging events. I find it fascinating that an affliction that has disrupted someone's life for years or even decades can completely disappear in a few EFT sessions, in a single day, or in some cases less than an hour.

In recent years, the problems associated with Post Traumatic Stress Disorder have been increasingly in the news. Everyone is looking for something, anything, that will help those who live with constant stress, fear, and anxiety, including the families and friends of those most affected.

It's true that much of this book focuses on military veterans, because the most obvious and noticed forms of PTSD occur in that population, but I'd like to remind everyone that PTSD is PTSD no matter what the cause —and that EFT works for all types of trauma as well as hundreds of other conditions.

I invite you to join me on a journey through a technique that is easy to learn, easy to use, and produces remarkable benefits for all whose lives are touched by Post-Traumatic Stress Disorder.

A Vital Guide for Reading This Book

In a nutshell, EFT is an emotional version of acupuncture, the centuries-old healing art still practiced in Traditional Chinese Medicine, except that we don't use needles. Instead, we stimulate the body's acupuncture meridians by tapping on them with our fingertips. This often brings forth astonishing results that are likely to be far beyond your expectations. The procedure is easy to learn, easy to use, and easy to share with others. You will learn the basics and more in this book.

EFT is good for everything. While this book focuses on EFT's use for Post-Traumatic Stress Disorder, or PTSD, I must emphasize *that the treatment of trauma represents but a tiny fraction of EFT's long list of successes.* For example, EFT is good for pain and physical symptoms of all kinds and it often works where nothing else will. It is also astonishingly useful for treating emotional issues of every type, and it reduces the typical psychotherapy process from months or years down to minutes or hours. Further, those wishing to improve their performance in sports, business, public speaking, or the bedroom will find EFT a valuable aid.

This book is like an encyclopedia. It is so comprehensive that it could easily be considered an "EFT Encyclopedia for PTSD." Most readers will find it a priceless resource because it contains approaches and concepts that you will not find in other health-related books, magazines, or reports.

This book is a how-to guide for counselors and health care practitioners. Those who already work with clients or patients whose lives are affected by PTSD know how time-consuming conventional therapies are and how limited their results can be. Psychologists, psychiatrists, and other experts who have witnessed EFT first-hand are usually stunned at how quickly it works and how effective it is. Although basic EFT is incredibly simple, when we work with complex issues like PTSD, there is much to be said for "the art of delivery," the shortcuts and sophisticated presentations that distinguish novices from experts. You can learn the basics of EFT in just a few minutes, but it takes time, study, and practice to understand and utilize its nuances. The examples, case reports, and descriptions presented here can help anyone go beyond the basics while incorporating EFT into his or her counseling sessions for improved results.

This book is a how-to guide for those who suffer from PTSD. There is much debate among health care practitioners as to what causes Post-Traumatic Stress Disorder and how it should be treated, with many warnings for those who suffer from PTSD against attempting to treat this problem themselves. However, I am convinced that if you follow the step-by-step guidelines described in Chapter Thirteen, the problems, complications, or adverse side effects experienced in other treatment methods are unlikely to materialize. Your best approach is to work with a counselor or practitioner who has experience with both PTSD and EFT, but if such support is not available, there is much you can do on your own to safely and effectively address your symptoms and their underlying causes.

This book contains creative approaches written by many EFT experts. EFT is an "open source" healing tool that encourages experimentation. This means that we start with an easy-to-learn, simple procedure that works beautifully in the majority of cases. After that, anyone can experiment with the process and develop other refinements. Thus, for your expanded education, I am sprinkling within this book the opinions, experiences, and creative approaches of EFT students and practitioners.

How to Learn EFT

There are several ways to learn EFT. You can start by reading the EFT Manual, which can be freely downloaded from www.EFTUniverse.com or purchased from retail and online booksellers as a paperback book, *The EFT Manual (EFT: Emotional Freedom Techniques)* by Gary Craig, published by Energy Psychology Press, 2008.

The manual describes the science behind EFT, its basic procedure, tips for applying it, case histories, how to correct factors that can interfere with EFT, shortcuts, and recommendations for improving results. You can read the entire manual on your computer, but most students print it out or have it printed at a copy center, then place it in a three-ring binder or have it bound for convenience. Some add blank pages for note taking, or they use Post-It® notes and highlighters to mark important sections for review.

My favorite way is to watch our DVDs, which show EFT in action in a variety of settings, from a hotel swimming pool ("Dave's Fear of Water") to the Veterans Administration Hospital where Vietnam War veterans used EFT to treat their PTSD ("Six Days at the V.A."), to live seminars in which people with all kinds of problems volunteered to be treated onstage. To help spread the word about EFT, these DVDs are economically priced, and they come with my written permission to make up to 100 copies of each and every disc to give away.

As I like to remind everyone, there is more human drama, inspiration, and humor in our videotaped seminars than there is in any reality television show!

The official EFT website, www.EFTUniverse.com, offers many resources including my online tutorial, which is a series of instructions, explanations, and exercises that can help you move from the most basic and fundamental EFT techniques to what I call the *art of delivery*, the combination of skill and talent that comes with experience and imagination.

Over 50 books about EFT have been written by practitioners, students, health care professionals, and other experts, providing instructions and all types of examples.

Still another way to learn EFT is to attend a workshop or demonstration conducted by an EFT instructor or practitioner. These are held in libraries, adult schools, restaurants, private homes, clinics, conference centers, offices, meeting rooms, and wherever people gather. You will get more out of these workshops if you first read the appropriate EFT books.

And there are many opportunities to learn EFT and hone your skills online. My EFT Insights Newsletter is called "The Heartbeat of EFT" because it features breaking news, reports from users on every topic imaginable, tips from our website, and links to practitioners. In addition, dozens of EFT practitioners have their own websites featuring helpful reports, and there are several EFT-related forums and chat groups whose members support each other with questions, answers, recommendations, and suggestions.

This book is designed to help you learn EFT and immediately take it to a new level. Throughout its chapters, you'll find explanations, examples, ideas, and scripts you can borrow. Best of all, the reports shared by EFT practitioners and students are actual examples of EFT in action.

Whether you are new to EFT or already an experienced "tapper," and whether you plan to use EFT in your profession or simply for yourself or to help a loved one, it is my pleasure to share this book with you. I know without a doubt that EFT can help just about anyone take control of his or her health and happiness and that the instructions and recommendations given here can completely transform and improve lives and relationships.

1

Post-Traumatic
Stress Disorder

Post-Traumatic Stress Disorder or PTSD is an anxiety disorder that develops after exposure to a frightening or terrifying event or ordeal in which grave physical harm took place or was threatened. It occurs in people of any age, including children and adolescents. Family members of victims can develop the condition as well. Depression, other anxiety disorders, and alcohol or drug abuse often accompany PTSD.

Definitions of PTSD vary, but most are based on *The Diagnostic and Statistical Manual of Mental Disorders, 4th. Edition,* better known as the DSM-IV, which is published by the American Psychiatric Association.

An official diagnosis of PTSD usually requires that at least one or more symptoms from each of the following categories be present for at least a month and that symptoms interfere with the patient leading a normal life.

- The person relives the event through nightmares or flashbacks, or the person has very strong mental and physical reactions when reminded of the event.

- The person avoids activities, thoughts, feelings, and conversations that remind him or her of the traumatic event or events, is unable to remember details about the event, or feels emotionally numb and detached from the present moment.

- The person loses interest in important activities, feels alone, is unable to experience normal emotions, or feels there is nothing to look forward to.

- The person can never relax, has trouble sleeping, feels irritable, overreacts when startled, can't concentrate, feels angry, and tries to be on guard at all times.

However, the definition of PTSD continues to evolve, and I think it's safe to say that anyone whose thoughts or behavior have been affected by a difficult event or situation is a likely candidate. To me, there is no dividing line between PTSD and trauma. Whether or not someone has been labeled with an official diagnosis of PTSD, the technique described here can help.

Events that trigger PTSD include violent personal assaults, natural disasters, manmade disasters, accidents, and military combat. Those experiencing the most pronounced PTSD symptoms include war veterans; survivors of terrorist attacks; survivors of devastating hurricanes, tornadoes, floods, tsunamis or tidal waves, volcanic eruptions, and other natural phenomena; plus survivors of accidents, rape, physical and sexual abuse, and other crimes; survivors of political persecution; immigrants fleeing violence or disaster; police officers, fire fighters, paramedics, emergency medical technicians, and rescue workers; hospital staff; and anyone who witnesses traumatic events.

Physical symptoms such as insomnia, headaches, immune system disorders, chest pain, numbness, gastro-intestinal distress, dizziness, fatigue, weight loss, weight gain, and other symptoms that stem from stress and anxiety often accompany PTSD.

It isn't easy living with someone who suffers from PTSD and its complications, which can include alcohol or drug abuse or addiction, chronic anxiety, depression, increased suicide risk, guilt, low self-esteem, panic attacks, fears, phobias, domestic violence, and unemployment, which is why so many spouses, children, parents, other relatives, and close friends of those who have PTSD develop symptoms themselves. PTSD is often accompanied by physical injuries, illnesses, and long hospitalizations.

Post-Traumatic Stress Disorder is believed to be significantly under-reported in the United States, so any statistics we read are guesses at best.

In the 1980s, 40 percent of Vietnam War veterans were estimated to have problems with drug abuse and almost half of those veterans had been divorced at least once.

Today military researchers estimate that 12 to 20 percent of Iraq war veterans experience the recurring nightmares, heightened anxiety, and emotional numbness that are synonymous with PTSD, and that half of all mental health disability claims involve it.

Some military psychiatrists report that the number of U.S. troops requiring treatment for PTSD may exceed

200,000. Others suggest that the military's PTSD population may be 27 percent of noncommissioned officers serving three or more tours.

The conventional treatments for PTSD include group discussions, or talk therapy; cognitive behavioral therapy, in which changes in thought produce changes in behavior; and exposure therapy, in which the person gradually and repeatedly relives or re-experiences a frightening event under controlled conditions. By far the most widely used treatments forPTSD are pharmaceutical, including the use of selective serotonin reuptake inhibitors (SSRIs) and other antidepressants.

While conventional approaches to PTSD do help some patients, their overall success rate is low, and even when they work well, progress is slow and involves ongoing treatment sessions.

In contrast, EFT can bring almost immediate results. I don't mean that everyone with PTSD will experience instant relief, but the majority of cases respond to EFT much more quickly than they do to conventional treatments.

On March 31, 2005, the *Union Tribune* in San Diego, California, published a story by staff writer Rick Rogers about how social workers, chaplains, and psychiatrists from Naval Medical Center San Diego and Camp Pendleton were learning EFT from instructor Sue Hannibal to help combat veterans alleviate psychological wounds.

In the article, Jeannie Ertl, a senior clinical social worker at the medical center, said, "EFT is tremendous for treating anxiety associated with Post-Traumatic Stress

Disorder." At that time she had tried the method on 15 patients, 12 of whom found it helpful at relieving or eliminating symptoms such as anxiety and stress. Ertl used EFT in conjunction with more conventional therapies.

The article then described Seaman Wilbur Hurley, a 20-year-old corpsman who had returned to Camp Pendleton the previous October after witnessing a young Marine kill himself while serving in Iraq.

"I felt like a black cloud was over my head every day," Hurley said. "I had vivid dreams of walking through fields of gore. I isolated myself from friends and family." Soon the nightmares were accompanied by panic attacks that interfered with his driving.

Following a friend's advice, Hurley made an appointment with Hannibal, who introduced him to EFT. "Once I started doing the tapping, an overwhelming calm came over me," Hurley said. "I had no cares or worries in the world. In fact, I left Sue's office singing. It was pretty much the greatest day of my life."

Hurley later concentrated on the worst cases he had seen while patching up Marines in Ramadi as well as focusing on the suicide to see whether anxiety would trigger another panic attack. "But I felt nothing," he said. "It wasn't there anymore."

In my experience, Seaman Hurley's response to EFT tapping is typical. People with all kinds of traumatic memories have been able to tap their stress and anxiety away so that the memories, even of unimaginably terrible events, no longer haunt them.

❋ ❋ ❋

I'm always interested in seeing PTSD from the perspective of those who suffer from its symptoms. The following is from a combat veteran who learned EFT in May of 2008. His report speaks for itself, as do the comments added by his wife.

A Marine Overcomes PTSD

by Sgt. Trent Miller

I spent 12 years in the U.S. Marines and U.S. Army. I was deployed to the Middle East four times, including to Desert Storm and OIF (Operation Iraqi Freedom). I have been home in Alexander, Arkansas, near Little Rock, since June of 2004.

When I first got back I was having a lot of trouble readjusting to things at home. I thought that I would be able to shake this set of problems plaguing me, but they kept getting worse. I would suffer from the inability to sleep, relax, attend gatherings, or be around any kind of stress. I would forget almost everything. I just wasn't myself anymore.

I went to the V.A. for help, which all vets should, but now I know why I had heard so many bad things about the V.A. I was prescribed medicine after medicine, dosage after dosage, but to no avail. My doctor said the next step was admitting myself to the V.A. hospital for electroshock therapy. There was no way I would subject myself to this. So, after four years of fighting with myself and the V.A., I was awarded a 60-percent disability.

I wasn't feeling any better, had thoughts of suicide, and my soul mate, my wife of ten years, was ready to leave me. I don't blame her for those thoughts. I was drinking heavily, mean towards her, and reclusive. While on a trip to Germany, my wife heard of EFT from a friend. Upon her return and with some research, she found a local practitioner, Dr. Steve Manire. She made contact with him and I agreed to meet him. He came to our home and told me about EFT. I wasn't exactly sold on the idea, but he said the results would be wondrous. I agreed to try. After the first two-hour session, I felt different. My body wasn't tired anymore, and I felt like I had taken my first breath of air in four years. My body was alive and tingling.

I thanked Dr. Manire for his time and agreed to continue working with him twice a week. I no longer have issues with sleeping or anxiety, and I actually look forward to the next day. I'm a different person. My wife and I are together and a lot stronger now. Dr. Manire has even been helping my wife with some of the issues she has faced since my return. I strongly recommend EFT to any vet.

This message is from Trent's wife, Gisela Miller:

How do you help a stubborn ex-Marine who suffers from PTSD?

For more than four years I tried to find help for my husband on how to handle life with PTSD but had no success in finding anything except medications that didn't work. I remember sitting in the big, ugly, uncomfortable waiting room at the V.A., looking around for any kind of brochure or information that would help us understand and cope with PTSD. To my big surprise, there was nothing. We were on our own. I was at the point where I had no energy left, was exhausted, and saw no end in sight.

PTSD was destroying our marriage. I felt that I had tried everything, but things kept getting worse. When I mentioned to my best friend that I was going to file for divorce, she suggested giving EFT a try. She had mentioned it before but I kept thinking, "Yeah, right, he's going to laugh at me once I tell him somebody is going to tap on his body to make him feel better."

But he did agree to try it, and in his first session he got amazing results. It was unbelievable—his facial features appeared more relaxed, he smiled, and he looked more peaceful. He now sleeps better, stays calm, no longer has anger outbursts, and is much more patient.

I cannot thank EFT enough for what it has done for us. It literally saved our marriage. I fell in love with my husband again. He is now the person he used to be, the man I fell in love with when I first met him. Even though it may take a while for him to completely recover, at least I see now that there is a light at the end of the tunnel!

If you are married to a veteran who suffers from PTSD, please give EFT a try.

Just a month after Trent began his EFT sessions, Dr. Manire reported, "I saw him again tonight, and he was doing so well that we really couldn't come up with anything to tap on! It looks as though Gisela's light at the end of the tunnel has arrived."

❊ ❊ ❊

Testing EFT with Combat Veterans

To put EFT to the test under controlled conditions, in March 2008 I brought nine veterans and two of their family members, all of whom were assessed for PTSD and related conditions, to San Francisco for a research study in which they worked with EFT practitioners Carol Look, Lindsay Kenny, Sophia Cayer, Lori Lorenz, Ingrid Dinter, and myself. All group discussions and EFT sessions were conducted on-camera for a documentary movie.

I found the participants by posting a notice on our EFT website asking for volunteers. Right away I got 30 or 40 responses, but most of those were from friends or relatives of veterans with PTSD. Only a few vets applied on their own behalf, which is what I expected from a group that is cautious and skeptical by nature.

My goal was to include veterans from several different wars, not just recent conflicts, and I especially wanted to work with vets who had serious problems with PTSD. I didn't want mild PTSD symptoms. My main consideration as I went through the applications and interviewed people by phone was, "How challenging can this case be?" Our observers included a psychiatrist and a psychologist, both of whom work with PTSD and both of whom agreed that my choices were "over the top" in severity. I also wanted to include some family members and women as well as men.

The 11 participants ranged in age from 26 to 61. Four were women, two of whom were veterans. One was the mother of a young vet who was also a participant, and she had some severe PTSD issues herself as a result of dealing with her son's behavior after he returned from Iraq. Another was a participant's wife, who had terrible migraine headaches and lived in a constant state of fear because whenever her husband became upset, he would run around the house cocking a loaded gun.

The veterans had fought in Vietnam, the Gulf War, and Iraq. Their physical disabilities included old injuries, ALS (Amyotrophic Lateral Sclerosis, or Lou Gherig's disease), and osteoarthirits. Two used wheelchairs.

When I first met everyone, I could feel and practically see a dark cloud hanging over the room. These people were curious enough to attend but they were extremely cautious, withdrawn, and doubting. None of them expected EFT to work. At the end, they gave us a standing ovation. I figure that if EFT can achieve spectacular success among combat veterans, it can be just as successful with everyone else.

The veterans' study used standard psychological evaluations—the SA-45 (Symptom Assessment 45) and PCL-M (Post-Traumatic Stress Disorder Checklist – Military)—as well as sleep diaries. Baseline measurements were obtained 30 days prior to treatment, immediately before treatment began, at the conclusion of the five-day study, and again 30 days and 90 days after that.

The PCL-M is a self-assessment tool used by the military to score PTSD. It lists 17 items and asks respondents to report how much they were bothered by a problem in the last month using a 1-to-5 scale to measure intensity. A sample question is, "In the past month, how much have you been bothered by repeated, disturbing memories, thoughts, or images of a stressful military experience?"

The SA-45 is a 45-question assessment of nine psychological symptoms including anxiety, depression, and hostility.

Because insomnia and nightmares are common among veterans, participants completed a seven-day sleep diary showing how alert they felt upon waking, how many times they woke during the night, the quality of their function during the day, and how they assessed the quality of their sleep.

The subjects worked with EFT for two or three hours per day for five days, after which they were re-evaluated. By that time their test scores for PTSD had dropped so significantly that they were now in the "normal" range, and their self-reported insomnia also decreased. When the subjects were re-tested 30 days later, they retained almost all of the gains they experienced during the study.

In the following graph, the first column shows the participants' PTSD scores prior to treatment, which were then very high, over 60. The middle column shows how after treatment, their PTSD scores fell dramatically, to just over 20. Thirty days after treatment, as shown by the third column, their PTSD scores rose slightly but remained well below their original highs. The dark gray at the bottom of each column shows the lowest possible scores for the tests.

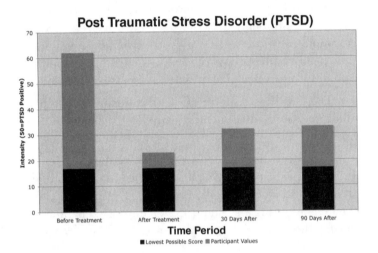

Post Traumatic Stress Disorder (PTSD)

One of the study's subjects, a man in his late fifties, gave us this report:

"I'm a Vietnam veteran and I suffer from PTSD. At the V.A., I was also diagnosed as bipolar or manic depressive. I have nightmares. I have spent since 1997 in hospitals and institutions. I take meds for bipolar. It's hard to get any alternative treatment at the V.A. My world wasn't that great. Everything in my life was a major challenge. When I came to the EFT event, I had no clue what I was walking into. I had never been to the west coast or on a plane. I hate flying.

"One of my Vietnam War memories involved an enemy attack where I had to pull bodies out of the rubble. I talked about it at the EFT event and the intensity was so bad I had to leave the room because I felt I was going to puke. Now that EFT has been done on it, I can think about the same incident with little or no intensity. It is no longer part of my dreams. That's a kind of freedom I never thought I would have. Other war memories faded as well. The event was outstanding.

"I've been doing EFT ever since then. The changes in my life are 100 percent totally different. Once you start EFT it's a totally different way to handle things. Everything like sleep and nightmares and suicide thoughts all come into a place where a total turnaround happens. I can't explain it. I want to help other veterans get this stuff. I'll go on a plane anywhere to help other veterans with EFT."

Additional research is going on as well. In one study, Iraq War veterans undergoing six biweekly hourlong EFT sessions experienced improvements in their depression, anxiety, and PTSD scores. In another, a single hour-long EFT session resulted in large drops in blood cortisol levels, indicating a positive effect on stress biochemistry.

Follow-up studies of most PTSD therapies have shown that improvements can be temporary, with symptoms returning over time. But six months after EFT treatments for phobias and anxiety, subjects continued to show improvement. I expect that the same will be true for those who use EFT to relieve their PTSD symptoms.

At the same time, because PTSD can be a complex problem with many layers or aspects, it's a mistake to think of EFT as a one-time cure-all treatment. Much depends on the skill of the practitioner, rapport between client and practitioner, the ability of the practitioner to help the client focus on specific memories, and the ability of the client to continue to practice EFT on his or her own.

But in the vast majority of cases, EFT is a fast, effective way to take the edge off of PTSD symptoms and related emotions and conditions.

※ ※ ※

One of the observers at our veterans' PTSD event was Stephen S. Nagy, M.D., a psychiatrist who is Board-certified in Adult Psychiatry by the American Board of Psychiatry and Neurology and certified by the American Society of Addiction Medicine. For the past two and a half years, Dr. Nagy has dealt primarily with patients who have Post-Traumatic Stress Disorder. Prior to that, he had extensive experience both in private practice and in community mental health settings. He has worked with severely and chronically psychiatrically ill individuals throughout his career.

Observing Veterans
with PTSD Being Treated with EFT

by Stephen S. Nagy, M.D.

I first heard about EFT from friends who talked about it as a treatment that is different, simple, and effective. I then met a couple of EFT practitioners.

I was especially interested in "Dave's Fear of Water," an episode in which Gary and Dave, a man who was too afraid to even put his face in the water, stood in a hotel swimming pool while they tapped about his phobia. A few minutes later, while watching Dave relax, laugh, and swim happily in the pool, I thought that that this videotaped session was either totally fraudulent and a hoax, or that EFT was something I needed to take a closer look at.

When I learned about the event being planned to treat veterans with PTSD in San Francisco in March 2008, I contacted Gary to ask if I could attend as an observer. He invited me to come. My travel, hotel, and other expenses were all paid for by me, and I did not receive compensation of any kind. I wanted to be a completely impartial observer. I spent most of the week sitting with the film crew as the EFT practitioners did their work. I was able to speak with the vets and the practitioners as well as attend the daily meetings to discuss treatment strategies and approaches. I had full access to the whole process from start to finish.

When I asked Gary how he chose the participants, he said he looked for the sickest people he could find. I would say that those who attended were representative of people who are severely afflicted with PTSD. It was definitely not a group of the "worried well."

What's interesting about PTSD in combat veterans is that it often takes about two years from the time they return home to fully develop symptoms. People deal with this type of stress however they can. The traditional approach is to get very, very drunk and stay that way. It's often more extreme in the military than what you see in civilian settings, as the problem of what to do with powerful emotions that remain active even though they have nothing to do with what's going on at the present moment is part of the combat veteran's daily experience.

When I arrived in San Francisco, I didn't assume that anyone would be instantly cured, but I was open to the possibility that at least some of the participants might experience improvement. By then I had reached the conclusion that EFT could probably help relieve PTSD symptoms, but I wondered whether the improvements would be temporary or permanent, and to what degree symptoms would return again or have a risk of returning. I also wondered whether this intense but short period of treatment, such as just a few minutes or maybe an hour or two, could help someone who had been suffering for many years after a painful event. If so, it would be a real breakthrough.

The conventional methods of treating PTSD have a limited set of expectations. One hopes that one can improve target symptoms like depression, anxiety, and nightmares, so that life becomes manageable. In the best setting, patients receive a combination of psychopharmacology, talk therapy, individual or one-on-one therapy, and some type of group therapy.

Symptoms of PTSD are rated using a self-reporting questionnaire, named the Post-Traumatic Stress Disorder Checklist, Military version, in which seventeen symptoms are rated from 1 to 5 by the individual, where the scale is:

1 = Not at all

2 = A little bit

3 = Moderately

4 = Quite a bit

5 = Extremely

Thus, the highest possible score is an 85 and an asymptomatic person would score a 17. The recognized scoring criteria require a score of 50 to make a diagnosis of military PTSD.

A 5- or 10-point change in a PCL-M score is regarded as a significant improvement. But in my experience, improvements occur only for a short time because various triggers can rekindle symptoms that frighten the person who has this diagnosis. If one is honest, one would have to say that PTSD is understood to be a permanent condition, one that waxes and wanes in symptom intensity.

Psychiatry views PTSD as a permanent change. Several interventions may lessen symptoms, including individual or group counseling, mindfulness training, and psychotropic medications. But this diagnosis is recognized as a basis for granting an individual permanent disability. I believe that anyone who has worked with individuals with PTSD sees that symptoms can wax and wane, and the goal of all conventional treatment is to reduce symptoms of hyperarousal, anxiety, and mood swings to the point that the afflicted individual improves. But no conventional treatment views this as a potentially reversible condition.

My own personal struggle as I have worked with individuals with PTSD has been to wish for a technique that could take them back to the state of emotional freedom and comfort that they had prior to their traumatizing experiences. It's as if their involuntary nervous system, which regulates the fight-flight and relaxation responses, got stuck in fight-flight, so that the individual has a very difficult time relaxing. With the most successful conventional treatment, the person's symptoms might subside to a point where he or she can resume a normal life, but there is always the risk that something will happen, such as an anniversary, a television news story, a newspaper or magazine article, 4th of July fireworks, or some other event that triggers memories that come flooding back, and the symptoms of hyperarousal, sleeplessness, fearfulness, and mood cycling all come back, too. These symptoms can be quite severe and take time and further treatment to subside.

I was Board-certified in Adult Psychiatry in 1982, and in the years since then I have seen many enthusiasms for conventional and alternative therapies come and go. None of them ever had as its expectation the goal that the person would be asymptomatic at the end of treatment. However, in several of the EFT sessions that I observed in San Francisco, this is what happened. Vets who arrived in a great deal of pain saw either a complete resolution of their symptoms or a very sizable reduction. I noticed that those with recent traumas got faster results, but even those who had been wrestling with inner demons for 30 or 40 years got quite good relief. Also, those whose war experiences weren't layered onto serious traumas from childhood got faster results than those whose war traumas were complicated by aspects from the past. I know that Gary Craig says that all traumas, however complicated, can eventually respond to EFT, especially with perseverance and the help of a skilled practitioner. If this is true, then this treatment offers much more therapeutic efficacy than any other approach that I have ever seen.

We started on Sunday night and I was able to sit in with the staff as they reviewed the participants' histories and the symptoms that were going to be targeted for treatment.

I felt it was very important to have some follow-up after one month and again after three months, and the vets completed the PCL-M at these times. The self-reports suggest that folks who got relief from their symptoms have sustained that improvement over time. They were all encouraged to continue tapping on their own after the week was over. It's of course hard to know exactly what they're doing and whether they are continuing to do EFT on themselves, but their reports indicate that they are markedly better than they were when they first came to the week of treatment, which was in some cases after years of conventional therapy.

When asked whether results like those that I witnessed in San Francisco would be considered a success if they were produced by conventional treatment, I have to say that if conventional treatment produced these same results, it would be considered to be miraculous, unexpected, and amazing.

What appeals to me about EFT is that it seems to give people a chance at putting old burdens aside and continuing to move forward in their lives. Many vets with severe PTSD exist indoors and away from human contact, always on guard and on alert, without the ability to enjoy life or find a fulfilling role. What makes this treatment attractive, after one leaps the initial small hurdle of the "oddness" of the tapping, is the effectiveness in reducing symptoms. But I think that what will ultimately sell EFT to vets who are skeptical of medical interventions is that the treatment does not have to be painful, does not involve medications, and can be self-administered. One does not have to re-experience difficult memories in order to alleviate them or take medications to put them away partially. There is a widespread assumption that if you're going to get better, you're going to have to pay for it, such as by reliving a painful experience all over again. That is in fact true for some therapies, but it isn't true for EFT.

Several times during the week of PTSD treatment in San Francisco, I saw veterans become so upset that they could not talk about the details of a memory. Without reliving the experience, they did the tapping and at the end of the session calmly said, "Here's what was bothering me so much." They then described the event without experiencing any of the emotional intensity that had upset them just a few minutes before. I find it very interesting that EFT can bring about significant physiological changes without the person having to put into words the memories or events that disturbed him, or without using medications.

EFT seems to be effective, substantially permanent, mostly painless, and usable by the individual for his or her own treatment if other aspects of a problem come up in the future. What would make it appealing to a large system faced with a lot of people with PTSD is that there's no cost for pharmaceuticals, someone can be brought out of a fairly dangerous situation relatively rapidly, the person can experience relief from intense inner pain quite quickly compared to the waiting time that's necessary for medications, there isn't any ongoing treatment expense because the treatment doesn't have to be continued indefinitely, and there aren't any of the complications that occur when patients become attached to the therapists they see weekly or monthly for years. When administered to new combat veterans, this treatment would give them a chance to go on to have a life after they have served. For vets who have been disabled for years with symptoms, it's not quite so simply beneficial, as they are out of the work force, dependent upon disability payments from the government, and are concerned that these benefits could be reduced or ended if they were able to work again.

If therapists and counselors want to help folks who have problems with anxiety, I think that EFT is something they should learn about. For those with PTSD or other symptoms of stress and anxiety, I think the overwhelming realization is that there is hope. They don't have to suffer eternally.

I know that people who feel hopeless think of death as a final release from suffering, and where PTSD is involved, the suffering is made worse by sleep deprivation, high anxiety, being easily startled, having impaired relations with other people, and being unable to feel love or affection. What I would most like people with PTSD to realize is that things like success, happiness, love, health, and good relationships are not lost forever. Watching this week's progress left me with the hopeful feeling that it could be possible to treat the painful symptoms of Post-Traumatic Stress Disorder and resolve them, possibly with some ongoing support. It seems that it really is possible to leave all of the anguish behind and go on with one's life.

At the time that I got my training, there was still the choice of going into psychoanalytically oriented training or one of the newer biologically oriented psychiatry training programs. In the psychoanalytically oriented program there were psychosomatic theories about bodily dysfunction originating in emotional reactions to events, situations, or people. The problem with that early theorizing was that there wasn't anything you could do with it. Nowadays, psychiatry has become a specialty of allopathic medicine, where you search for symptoms that might be amenable to treatment with pharmacologic agents such as antidepressants or antipsychotic drugs. The notion that the heart of what's going on is still in the individual is not really considered. Gary's approach is basically a psychosomatic formulation that goes straight to the physiology of the problem, using EFT to knock the props out from under the symptoms.

People always try to put a new experience into their own life or educational or intellectual context to make sense of it, and it's very interesting that this whole practice might have been more acceptable to conventional medicine if it had been developed 50 or 60 years ago, when it could have been seen as the therapeutic arm of psychoanalytically oriented psychiatry. I'm sure that the major hurdle that EFT faces is that people just don't think psychodynamically any more. They don't look at emotionally upsetting events as the origin or cause of physical symptoms.

The great challenge of the human condition is settling internal agitation. Goodness knows, we go through life having conflicts with other people and with a world which simply doesn't follow our expectations. We seem to have been hard-wired to hold resentment, irritations, angers, and grudges, all of which ultimately eat people from the inside out. The great challenge of living is to let go of injuries done to us, accept the lessons from experiences that we go through, and to forgive others for what they may have done or not done. The benefits of doing so are primarily for ourselves, so that we can move forward and no longer have those negative feelings as part of our day-to-day existence. From what I have seen, EFT seems to help this life challenge hugely. The positive effect of EFT in this respect is enormous.

One of the legacies of the Middle East wars is traumatic brain injury, or TBI. It's also known as closed head injury. This type of injury can produce major problems with short-term memory and complex reasoning. The person can experience cognitive dysfunction of many kinds. You can't be on street patrol in Iraq without experiencing some kind of blast injury, so many if not most veterans returning from Iraq have at least some TBI damage. Conventional medicine has very little to offer TBI patients, but I think EFT holds great promise for treating them.

I observed a videotape of a woman who suffered from problems relating to balance, light sensitivity, and short-term memory loss after receiving a concussion in a car accident. Six years after the accident, none of the therapies her physicians prescribed had made much of a difference, and she arrived at one of Gary's workshops needing a walking stick. Her response to EFT was amazing. After tapping, she dropped the walking stick and danced around the parking lot, exclaiming with joy over the things she could suddenly do, saying she couldn't wait to show her doctors. EFT could be an important treatment tool for TBI, whatever its origin.

❈ ❈ ❈

Research Using EFT to Treat PTSD
by Dawson Church, PhD

When Gary Craig and his team of volunteers were working with the 11 veterans and their family members in San Francisco, we collected and analyzed data on how the psychological conditions of the veterans changed. The result was a scientific study that was published in the peer-reviewed psychology journal *Traumatology*. The chart on page 34 is drawn from that study. This type of research is useful in validating EFT for psychologists working in the V.A. system and private practices. The reference for this study, in case you would like to provide the information to a health care provider, is: Church, D. (2009). The Treatment of Combat Trauma in Veterans using EFT (Emotional Freedom Techniques): A Pilot Protocol. *Traumatology,* March, 16(1), 55–65.

A second study, using six sessions of EFT to treat traumatic combat memories, found equally impressive results. PTSD scores of study participants dropped by 50%, depression by 49%, and anxiety by 46%. The results held three months later, and were statistically significant. The reference for this study is: Church,

D., & Geronilla, L. (2009). Psychological Symptom Change in Veterans after Six Sessions of EFT (Emotional Freedom Techniques): An Observational Study. *International Journal of Healing and Caring*, Jan 9:1.

Because of the excellent results being obtained by life coaches and therapists using EFT with veterans, and the encouraging findings of these two pilot studies, a large-scale ongoing study began in 2008. This is a form of experiment called a Randomized Clinical Trial or RCT, and is the Gold Standard of scientific proof. A network of therapists and life coaches, both within the V.A. system, and in private practices, has now been formed to connect veterans with those offering EFT. It's called the Iraq Vets Stress Project, and it has its own web site at www. StressProject.org. In my book *The Genie in Your Genes* (www.GenieBestseller.com) I show that there is a great deal of scientific proof for EFT, and my passion is to gather enough hard data to convince primary care providers like hospitals and clinics to start offering EFT routinely, and for medical caregivers to understand the link between emotional traumas and physical symptoms.

2

EFT's Basic Recipe

To appreciate how easy it is to learn EFT and teach it to those suffering from PTSD or any other disorder, here is a step-by-step description of the basic technique.

Defining the Problem

EFT sessions usually begin with a measurement of the person's discomfort using a scale from zero to 10. We call this the Intensity Meter. The discomfort being measured can be physical, such as pain, or it can be an emotion such as fear, anxiety, depression, or anger.

Measuring Intensity on the 0-to-10 Scale

0 – 1 – 2 – 3 – 4 – 5 – 6 – 7 – 8 – 9 – 10

none/mild discomfort/moderate discomfort/major discomfort/maximum pain

To help someone "tune into" his or her physical, emotional, or mental state, ask simple questions. For example, if the person is in pain, ask how much it hurts. Try this on yourself right now. Do you have a headache, is your knee sore, or does your back hurt?

If you have to be reminded that you're in pain, and when you look for it you remember that it's there but only just a little, you're in the "mild discomfort" zone and you'll give it a 1, 2, or 3. If it's slightly more intense, so that you can still move around but you're consciously aware of the pain, it's a 4, 5, or 6. If the pain is a major discomfort, something you can't forget about and it interferes with your ability to move, it's a 7, 8, or 9. A pain that's the maximum you can endure, which is as bad as it gets, is a 10.

It's a good idea to rate every problem before and after you apply EFT so that you can determine how much progress you're making. Don't worry if you find it difficult to select a specific number—sometimes Newbies get distracted by this part of the procedure and worry about whether it's a 5 or a 6, or a 2 or a 3. Using the 10-point scale gets easier with practice. Just give yourself a number to get started and it will soon become automatic. It helps to remind clients that there are no wrong answers here and that if they have trouble coming up with a specific number, a guess will work fine.

For reference, jot the number down and add a few notes about where the pain is located, how it interferes with your range of motion, and whether it hurts more when you move to the left or right, stand or sit, and so forth.

Another way to indicate the intensity of pain or discomfort is by stretching your arms wide apart for major pain and putting them close together for minor pain.

This method works well for children, who find it easier to express "big" and "small" with their hands than with a number scale.

Or you might visualize your discomfort on a thermometer, with the red line reaching the top for major pain and falling to the bottom for minor pain. Or you might visualize a meter that looks like an old-fashioned gas gauge, with minor pain at the zero or empty indicator on the left side and major pain on the 100 or full indicator on the right side.

The method you choose doesn't matter as long as it works for you. Keeping track of your pain's intensity before and after treatment is the easiest way to determine whether and how effectively the treatment is working.

The same scale works for feelings. First, focus on an event or memory or problem that has been bothering you. Now ask yourself the same questions you would ask a client or patient. How angry or anxious or depressed or upset are you on a scale from 0 to 10? If it doesn't bother you at all, you're at a zero. If you're at a 10, that's the maximum you can endure. Get in the habit of starting each tapping session with an intensity measurement and make a note of it.

Now, borrowing some pages from the EFT manual, I'd like to introduce you to the Basic Recipe, the formula that is the foundation of this technique.

The Basic Recipe

A recipe has certain ingredients which must be added in a certain order. If you are baking a cake, for example, you must use sugar instead of pepper and you must add the sugar before you put it in the oven. Otherwise... no cake.

Basic EFT is like a cake recipe. It has specific ingredients that go together in a specific way. Just as someone who is learning to cook will get best results from following tried and true instructions, someone who is new to EFT will do well to learn the basic recipe. An accomplished chef will take a different approach, and so can you once you master the fundamentals.

Although I am going to some length to describe it in detail, the Basic Recipe is very simple and easy to do. *Once memorized, each round of it can be performed in about one minute.* It will take some practice, of course, but after a few tries the whole process will becomes so familiar that you can bake that emotional freedom cake in your sleep. You will then be well on your way to mastery of EFT and all the rewards it provides.

Let me interject here that various *shortcuts* are available and described later in this book and in our trainings. I am describing the *full* Basic Recipe here because it provides an important foundation to the whole process. Proficient practitioners will want to use the shortcuts and other advanced techniques because they cut the average time involved by at least half and they greatly improve results, but the Basic Recipe is the place to begin.

The full Basic Recipe consists of four ingredients, two of which are identical. They are:

1. The Setup

2. The Sequence

3. The 9 Gamut Procedure

4. The Sequence

Ingredient #1: The Setup

Applying the Basic Recipe is something like going bowling. In bowling, there is a machine that sets up the pins by picking them up and arranging them in perfect order at the end of the alley. Once this "setup" is done, all you need to do is roll the ball down the alley to knock over the pins.

In a similar manner, the Basic Recipe has a beginning routine to "set up" your energy system as though it was a set of bowling pins. This routine (called the Setup) is vital to the whole process and prepares the energy system so that the rest of the Basic Recipe (the ball) can do its job.

Your energy system, of course, is not really a set of bowling pins. It is a set of subtle electric circuits. I present this bowling analogy only to give you a sense for the purpose of the Setup and the need to *make sure your energy system is properly oriented before attempting to remove its disruptions.*

Your energy system is subject to a form of electrical interference which can block the balancing effect of these tapping procedures. When present, this interfering blockage must be removed or the Basic Recipe will not work. Removing it is the job of the Setup.

Technically speaking, this interfering blockage takes the form of a *polarity reversal* within your energy system. This is different from the *energy disruptions* which cause your negative emotions.

Another analogy may help us here. Consider a flashlight or any other device that runs on batteries. If the batteries aren't there, it won't work. Equally important, *the batteries must be installed properly.* You've noticed, I'm sure, that batteries have + and - marks on them. Those marks indicate their *polarity.* If you line up those + and - marks according to the instructions, the electricity flows normally and your flashlight works fine.

But what happens if you put the batteries in backwards? Try it sometime. The flashlight will not work. It acts as if the batteries have been removed. That's what happens when polarity reversal is present in your energy system. It's like your batteries are in backwards. I don't mean that you stop working altogether—you don't turn "toes up" and die—but your progress does become arrested in some areas.

This polarity reversal has an official name. It is called Psychological Reversal and it represents a fascinating discovery with wide-ranging applications *in all areas of healing and personal performance.*

It is the reason why some diseases are chronic and respond very poorly to conventional treatments. It is also the reason why some people have such a difficult time losing weight or giving up addictive substances. It is, quite literally, the cause of self sabotage.

Psychological Reversal is caused by self-defeating, negative thinking which often occurs subconsciously and thus outside of your conscious awareness. On average, it will be present—and thus hinder EFT—about 40 percent of the time. Some people have very little of it (this is rare) while others are beset by it most of the time (this also is rare). Most people fall somewhere in between these two extremes. Psychological reversal doesn't create any feelings within you, so you won't know if it is present or not. Even the most positive people are subject to it, including yours truly.

When psychological reversal is present, it will stop any attempt at healing, including EFT, dead in its tracks. Therefore, *it must be corrected if the rest of the Basic Recipe is going to work.*

Being true to the 100-percent overhaul concept, we correct for Psychological Reversal *even though it might not be present.* It only takes 8 or 10 seconds to do and, if it isn't present, no harm is done. If it is present, however, a major impediment to your success will be out of the way.

That being said, here's how the Setup works. There are two parts to it. You repeat an affirmation three times while you rub the "Sore Spot" or, alternatively, tap the "Karate Chop" point. (These will be explained shortly.)

The Affirmation

Since the cause of Psychological Reversal involves negative thinking, it should be no surprise that the correction for it includes a neutralizing affirmation. Such is the case and here it is.

Even though I have this _____, I deeply and completely accept myself.

The blank is filled in with a brief description of the problem you want to address. Here are some examples.

Even though I have this <u>pain in my lower back</u>, I deeply and completely accept myself.

Even though I have this <u>anger towards my father</u>, I deeply and completely accept myself.

Even though I have this <u>war memory</u>, I deeply and completely accept myself.

Even though I have these <u>nightmares</u>, I deeply and completely accept myself.

Even though I have this <u>craving for alcohol</u>, I deeply and completely accept myself.

Even though I have this <u>depression</u>, I deeply and completely accept myself.

This is only a partial list, of course, because the possible issues that are addressable by EFT are endless. You can also vary the acceptance phrase by saying:

> *"I accept myself even though I have this* _____ _____."*

> *"Even though I have this* _____, *I deeply and profoundly accept myself."*

> *"I love and accept myself even though I have this* _____."*

All of these affirmations are correct because they follow the same general format. That is, they acknowledge the problem and create self acceptance despite the existence of the problem.

That is what's necessary for the affirmation to be effective. You can use any of them but I suggest you use the recommended one because it is easy to memorize and has a good track record of getting the job done.

It doesn't matter whether you believe the affirmation or not. Just say it. It is better to say it with feeling and emphasis, but saying it routinely will usually do the job. It is best to say it out loud, but if you are in a social situation where you prefer to mutter it under your breath, or do it silently, then go ahead. It will probably be effective.

To add to the effectiveness of the affirmation, the Setup also includes the simultaneous rubbing of a "Sore Spot" or tapping on the "Karate Chop" point. They are described next.

The Sore Spot

There are two Sore Spots and it doesn't matter which one you use. They are located in the upper left and right portions of the chest and you find them as follows:

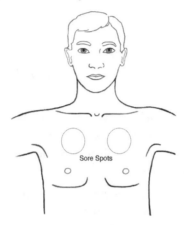

The Sore Spot

Go to the base of the throat about where a man would knot his tie. Poke around in this area and you will find a U shaped notch at the top of your sternum (breastbone). From the top of that notch go down 2 or 3 inches toward your navel and then move over 2 or 3 inches to your left (or right). You should now be in the upper left (or right) portion of your chest. If you press vigorously in that area (within a 2-inch radius) you will find a "Sore Spot." This is the place you will need to rub while saying the affirmation.

This spot is usually sore or tender when you rub it vigorously because lymphatic congestion occurs there. When you rub it, you are dispersing that congestion.

Fortunately, after a few episodes the congestion is all dispersed and the soreness goes away. Then you can rub it with no discomfort whatsoever.

I don't mean to overplay the soreness you may feel. It's not like you will have massive, intense pain by rubbing this Sore Spot. It is certainly bearable and should cause no undue discomfort. If it does, then lighten up your pressure a little.

Also, if you've had some kind of operation in that area of the chest or if there's any medical reason whatsoever why you shouldn't be probing around in that specific area then *switch to the other side.* Both sides are equally effective. In any case, if there is any doubt, consult your health practitioner before proceeding. Or tap the "Karate Chop" point instead.

The Karate Chop Point

The Karate Chop (KC) Point

The Karate Chop point (abbreviated **KC**) is located at the center of the fleshy part of the outside of your hand (either hand) between the top of the wrist and the base of the baby finger or, stated differently, it is the part of your hand you would use to deliver a karate chop.

Instead of rubbing it as you would the Sore Spot, you vigorously *tap* the Karate Chop point with the fingertips of the index finger and middle finger—or all fingers—of the other hand. While you *could* use the Karate Chop point of either hand, it is usually most convenient to tap the Karate Chop point of the non-dominant hand with the fingertips of the dominant hand. If you are right-handed, tap the Karate Chop point on the left hand with the fingertips of the right hand. If you are left-handed, tap the Karate Chop point on your right hand with the fingertips of your left hand.

If for some reason you are not able to use both hands, tap the Karate Chop point of one hand against any surface—a table, desk, the arm of a chair, or even your thigh. This point will also be effective if someone else taps on it for you.

Should you use the Sore Spot or the Karate Chop point? After years of experience with both methods, it has been determined that rubbing the Sore Spot is a bit more effective than tapping the Karate Chop point. It doesn't have a commanding lead by any means but it *is* preferred.

Because the Setup is so important in clearing the way for the rest of the Basic Recipe to work, I urge you to use the Sore Spot rather than the Karate Chop point. It puts the odds a little more in your favor. However, the Karate Chop point is perfectly useful and will clear out any interfering blockage in the vast majority of cases. So feel free to use it if the Sore Spot is inappropriate for any reason.

You will notice that in our videotaped seminars, I often instruct people to tap the Karate Chop point instead of rubbing the Sore Spot. That's because it is easier to teach when I'm onstage.

Now that you understand the parts to the Setup, performing it is easy. You create a word or short phrase to fill in the blank in the affirmation and then *simply repeat the affirmation, with emphasis, three times while continuously rubbing the Sore Spot or tapping the Karate Chop point.*

That's it. After a few practice rounds, you should be able to perform the Setup in 8 seconds or so. Now, with the Setup properly performed, you are ready for the next ingredient in the Basic Recipe, which is the Sequence.

Ingredient #2: The Sequence

The Sequence is very simple in concept. It involves tapping on the end points of the major energy meridians in the body and is the method by which the energy block (which I often refer to as a "zzzzzt") in the energy system is balanced out. Before locating these points for you, however, you need a few tips on how to carry out the tapping process.

Tapping Tips:

- You can tap with either hand but it is usually more convenient to do so with your dominant hand (your right hand if you are right-handed or your left hand if you are left-handed).

- Alternatively, you can tap with both hands. Tapping with both hands at the same time is preferred by many practitioners and students.

- Tap with the fingertips of your index finger and middle finger. This covers a little larger area than just tapping with one fingertip and allows you to cover the tapping points more easily.

- Alternatively, you can tap with three fingertips on each hand or even four. Experiment to find out which arrangement feels most comfortable for you.

- Tap solidly but never so hard as to hurt or bruise yourself.

- Tap about seven times on each of the tapping points. I say about seven times because you will be repeating a "reminder phrase" (explained later) while tapping and it will be difficult to count at the same time. If you are a little over or a little under seven (five to nine, for example) that will be sufficient.

Most of the tapping points exist on either side of the body. It doesn't matter which side you use nor does it matter if you switch sides during the Sequence. For example, you can tap under your right eye and, later in the Sequence, tap under your left arm.

The points: Each energy meridian has two end points. For the purposes of the Basic Recipe, you need only tap on one end to balance out any disruptions that may exist in it. These end points are near the surface of the body and are thus more readily accessed than other points along the meridians that may be more deeply buried. What follows are instructions on how to locate the end points of those meridians that are important to the Basic Recipe. Taken together and done in the order presented they form the Sequence.

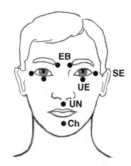

EB, SE, UE, UN and Ch Points

Eyebrow: At the beginning of the eyebrow, just above and to one side of the nose. This point is abbreviated **EB** for beginning of the **E**ye**B**row.

Side of Eye: On the bone bordering the outside corner of the eye. This point is abbreviated **SE** for **S**ide of the **E**ye.

Under Eye: On the bone under an eye about 1 inch below your pupil. This point is abbreviated **UE** for **U**nder the **E**ye.

Under Nose: On the small area between the bottom of your nose and the top of your upper lip. This point is abbreviated **UN** for **U**nder the **N**ose.

Chin: Midway between the point of your chin and the bottom of your lower lip. Although it is not directly on the point of the chin, we call it the chin point because it is descriptive enough for people to understand easily. This point is abbreviated **Ch** for **Ch**in.

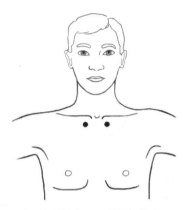

The Collarbone (CB) Points

Collarbone: The junction where the sternum (breast-bone), collarbone, and first rib meet. Place your forefinger on the U-shaped notch at the top of the breastbone (where a man would knot his tie). Move down toward the navel 1 inch and then go to the left (or right) about 1 inch. This point is abbreviated **CB** for **C**ollar**B**one *even though it is not on the collarbone (or clavicle) per se*. It is at the *beginning* of the collarbone.

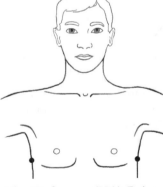

The Underarm (UA) Points

Underarm: On the side of the body, at a point even with the nipple (for men) or in the middle of the bra strap (for women). It is about 4 inches below the armpit. This point is abbreviated **UA** for **U**nder the **A**rm.

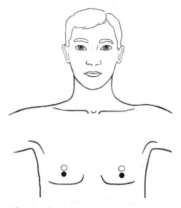

The Below Nipple (BN) Points

Below Nipple: For men, one inch below the nipple. For ladies, where the underskin of the breast meets the chest wall. This point is abbreviated **BN** for **B**elow **N**ipple.

The Thumb (Th) Point

Thumb: On the outside edge of your thumb at a point even with the base of the thumbnail. This point is abbreviated **Th** for **Th**umb.

The Index Finger (IF) Point

Index Finger: On the side of your index finger (the side facing your thumb) at a point even with the base of the fingernail. This point is abbreviated **IF** for **I**ndex **F**inger.

The Middle Finger (MF) Point

Middle Finger: On the side of your middle finger (the side closest to your thumb) at a point even with the base of the fingernail. This point is abbreviated **MF** for **M**iddle **F**inger.

The Baby Finger (BF) Point

Baby Finger: On the inside of your baby finger (the side closest to your thumb) at a point even with the base of the fingernail. This point is abbreviated **BF** for **B**aby Finger.

The Karate Chop (KC) Point

Karate Chop: The last point is the Karate Chop Point...which has been previously described under the section on the Setup. It is located in the middle of the fleshy part on the outside of the hand between the top of the wrist bone and the base of the baby finger. It is abbreviated **KC** for **K**arate **C**hop.

The abbreviations for these points are summarized below in the same order as given above.

EB = **B**eginning of the **EyeB**row

SE = **S**ide of the **E**ye

UE = **U**nder the **E**ye

UN = **U**nder the **N**ose

Ch = **Ch**in

CB = **B**eginning of the **C**ollar**B**one

UA = **U**nder the **A**rm

BN = **B**elow the **N**ipple

Th = **Th**umb

IF = **I**ndex **F**inger

MF = **M**iddle **F**inger

BF = **B**aby **F**inger

KC = **K**arate **C**hop

Please notice that these tapping points proceed *down the body*. That is, each tapping point is *below* the one before it. That should make it a snap to memorize. A few trips through it and it should be yours forever.

Note that the ring finger is not included in this list because it is considered redundant or unnecessary. However, many EFT practitioners include it for convenience.

Also note that the **BN** point has been added since our introductory trainings. It was originally left out because it was awkward for ladies to tap while in social situations, such as in restaurants, etc. Even though the EFT results have been superb without it, I include it now for completeness.

Ingredient #3: The 9 Gamut Procedure

The 9 Gamut Procedure is, perhaps, the most bizarre looking process within EFT. Its purpose is to "fine tune" the brain and it does so via some eye movements and some humming and counting. Through connecting nerves, certain parts of the brain are stimulated when the eyes are moved. Likewise the right side of the brain (the creative side) is engaged when you hum a song and the left side (the digital side) is engaged when you count.

The 9 Gamut Procedure is a 10-second process in which nine "brain stimulating" actions are performed while continuously tapping on one of the body's energy points, the Gamut point. It has been found, after years of experience, that this routine can add efficiency to EFT and hastens your progress towards emotional freedom, especially when *sandwiched* between 2 trips through The Sequence.

One way to help memorize the Basic Recipe is to look at it as though it is a ham sandwich. The Setup is the preparation for the ham sandwich and the sandwich itself consists of two slices of bread (the Sequence) with the ham, or middle portion, as the 9 Gamut Procedure.

The Gamut Point

To do the 9 Gamut Procedure, you must first locate the Gamut point. It is on the back of either hand and is 1/2 inch behind the midpoint between the knuckles at the base of the ring finger and the little finger.

If you draw an imaginary line between the knuckles at the base of the ring finger and little finger and consider that line to be the base of an equilateral triangle whose other sides converge to a point (apex) in the direction of the wrist, then the gamut point would be located at the apex of the triangle.

Next, you must perform nine different actions while tapping the Gamut point continuously. These 9 Gamut actions are:

1. Close your eyes.

2. Open your eyes.

3. Look down hard right while holding your head steady.

4. Look down hard left while holding your head steady.

5. Roll your eyes in a circle as though your nose is at the center of a clock and you are trying to see all the numbers in order. Hold your head steady.

6. Roll your eyes in a circle in the reverse direction. Hold your head steady.

7. Hum two seconds of a song (I usually suggest "Happy Birthday").

8. Count rapidly from 1 to 5.

9. Hum two seconds of a song again.

Note that these nine actions are presented in a certain order and I suggest that you memorize them in the order given. However, you can mix the order up if you wish so long as you do all nine of them *and* you perform the last three together as a unit. That is, you hum for two seconds, then count, then hum the song again, in that order. Years of experience have proven this to be important.

Also, note that for some people humming "Happy Birthday" causes resistance because it brings up memories of unhappy birthdays. In this case, you can either use EFT on those unhappy memories and resolve them, or you can side-step this issue for now by substituting some other song.

Ingredient #4: The Sequence (again)

The fourth and last ingredient in the Basic Recipe was explained above. It is an identical trip through The Sequence.

The Reminder Phrase

Once memorized, the Basic Recipe becomes a lifetime friend. It can be applied to an almost endless list of emotional and physical problems and provides relief from most of them. However, there's one more concept we need to develop before we can apply the Basic Recipe to a given problem. It's called the Reminder Phrase.

When a football quarterback throws a pass, he aims it at a particular receiver. He doesn't just throw the ball in the air and hope someone will catch it. Likewise, the Basic Recipe needs to be aimed at a specific problem. Otherwise, it will bounce around aimlessly with little or no effect. You "aim" the Basic Recipe by applying it while "tuned in" to the problem from which you want relief. This tells your system which problem needs to be the receiver.

Remember the discovery statement which states:

"The cause of all negative emotions is a disruption in the body's energy system."

Negative emotions come about because you are tuned into certain thoughts or circumstances which, in turn, cause your energy system to disrupt. Otherwise, you function normally. One's fear of heights is not present, for example, while one is reading the comic section of the Sunday newspaper and therefore not tuned in to the problem.

Tuning in to a problem can be done by simply thinking about it. In fact, tuning in *means* thinking about it. Thinking about the problem will bring about the energy disruptions involved, which then, and only then, can be balanced by applying the Basic Recipe. Without tuning in to the problem, thereby creating those energy disruptions, the Basic Recipe does nothing.

Tuning in is seemingly a very simple process. You merely think about the problem while applying the Basic Recipe. That's it, at least in theory.

However, you may find it a bit difficult to consciously think about the problem while you are tapping, humming, counting, etc. That's why I'm introducing a Reminder Phrase that you can repeat continually while you are performing the Basic Recipe.

The Reminder Phrase is simply a word or short phrase that describes the problem and that you repeat out loud each time you tap one of the points in the Sequence. In this way you continually "remind" your system about the problem you are working on.

The best Reminder Phrase to use is usually identical to what you choose for the affirmation you use in the Setup. For example, if you are working on a fear of public speaking, the Setup affirmation would go like this:

Even though I have this <u>fear of public speaking</u>, I deeply and completely accept myself.

Within this affirmation, the underlined words, <u>fear of public speaking</u>, are ideal candidates for use as the Reminder Phrase.

I sometimes use a shorter version of this Reminder Phrase when in seminars. I might, for example, use "public speaking fear" or just "public speaking" instead of the somewhat longer version shown above. That's just one of the shortcuts we have grown accustomed to after years of experience with these techniques. For your purposes, however, you can simplify your life by just using the identical words for the Reminder Phrase as you use for the affirmation in the Setup.

Now here's an interesting point that you will most certainly notice on our audios and some of our videos. *I don't always have people repeat a Reminder Phrase.* That's because I have discovered over time that simply stating the affirmation during the Setup is usually sufficient to "tune in" to the problem at hand. The subconscious mind usually locks on to the problem throughout the Basic Recipe even though all the tapping, humming, counting, etc., would seem to be distracting.

But this is not *always* true and, with extensive training and experience, one can recognize whether or not using the Reminder Phrase is necessary. As stated, it is not usually necessary but *when it is necessary it is really necessary and must be used.*

What's beautiful about EFT is that you don't need to have my experience in this regard. You don't have to be able to figure out whether or not the Reminder Phrase is necessary. You can just *assume* it is always necessary and thereby assure yourself of always being tuned in to the problem by simply repeating the Reminder Phrase as instructed. It does no harm to repeat the Reminder Phrase when it is not necessary, and it will serve as an invaluable tool when it is. This is part of the 100-percent overhaul concept mentioned earlier. We do many things in each round of the Basic Recipe that may not be necessary for a given problem. But when a particular part of the Basic Recipe *is* necessary, *it is absolutely critical.*

It does no harm to include everything, even what may be unnecessary, and *it only takes one minute per round.* This includes *always* repeating the Reminder Phrase each time you tap a point during The Sequence. It costs nothing to include it, not even time, because it can be repeated within the same time it takes to tap each energy point seven times. For example:

headache	*anger towards my father*
war memory	*stiffness in my neck*
nightmares	*craving for alcohol*

Subsequent Round Adjustments

Let's say you are using the Basic Recipe for some problem (fear, headache, anger, etc.). Sometimes the problem will simply vanish after just one round while, at other times, one round provides only partial relief. When only partial relief is obtained, you will need to do one or more additional rounds.

Those subsequent rounds have to be adjusted slightly for best results. Here's why: One of the main reasons why the first round doesn't always completely eliminate a problem is because of the re-emergence of Psychological Reversal, that interfering blockage that the Setup is designed to correct.

This time, Psychological Reversal shows up in a somewhat different form. Instead of blocking your progress altogether it now blocks any *remaining* progress. You have already made some headway but became stopped part way toward complete relief because Psychological Reversal entered in a manner that kept you from *getting any better still.*

Since the subconscious mind tends to be very literal, the subsequent rounds of the Basic Recipe need to address the fact that you are working on the *remaining problem.* Accordingly, the affirmation contained within the Setup has to be adjusted, as does the Reminder Phrase.

Here's the adjusted format for the Setup affirmation:

*Even though I **still** have **some** of this _____, I deeply and completely accept myself.*

Please note the emphasized words (*still* and *some*) and how they change the thrust of the affirmation toward the *remainder* of the problem. It should be easy to make this adjustment and, after a little experience, you will fall into it quite naturally.

The Reminder Phrase is also easily adjusted. Just put the word *"remaining"* before the previously used phrase. For example:

remaining headache   **remaining** nightmares

If your pain or discomfort disappears but then returns, simply repeat EFT's Basic Recipe and the "remaining pain" reminder phrase described above.

Optional Points

As EFT spread to those with a knowledge of acupuncture, many students and practitioners began to add tapping points. There are hundreds of acupuncture points on the human body—in fact, it's just about impossible to tap yourself anywhere without hitting one or more of them—but the most popular optional points in EFT circles are probably the top of the head and points on the wrists and ankles. None of these points are mentioned in the EFT Manual. Feel free to experiment with any of them.

Top of Head. Run an imaginary string over your head from the top of one ear to the top of the other. The highest point that the string reaches is the Top of Head point. It is set slightly back from the center of the top of your head.

Wrists. Several meridians run through the inside and outside of the wrist. An easy way to stimulate all of the wrist points is to cross your wrists and tap them together (about where your wristwatch would be), inside wrist against inside wrist, inside wrist against outside wrist, and outside wrist against outside wrist.

Ankle Points. Several meridians run through the ankles. These are less widely used because they're less convenient, but many EFTers include them from time to time. To stimulate these points, simply tap on all sides of either or both ankles.

In the reports shared by EFT users in our online newsletter, you'll see other points mentioned, including some that are used in combination. I don't personally use these points or combinations so I won't elaborate on them here. EFT is so flexible and versatile that I am never surprised when any acupressure tapping combined with focused thought produces good results.

Putting It All Together

Now that you have met the ingredients of our Basic Recipe, here is how a complete EFT treatment works using the Basic Recipe. For this example, we'll focus on a physical symptom—a headache—but we will use the same basic procedure to address other aspects of Post-Traumatic Stress Disorder. Most people with PTSD feel anxious when they encounter EFT for the first time, and their anxiety produces physical symptoms such as headaches, a feeling of tightness in the stomach, nausea, dizziness, tense shoulder muscles, or an inability to take a deep, relaxed breath. Any of these symptoms can be an excellent "first problem" to treat with EFT.

What is the problem? I have a headache.

How bad is it? It's pretty serious. On a scale from 1 to 10, it's an 8.

Setup: Tap the Karate Chop point or rub the Sore Spot while saying:

Even though I have this headache, I fully and completely accept myself.

Even though I have this headache, I fully and completely accept myself.

Even though I have this headache, I fully and completely accept myself.

The Sequence: Tap each point while repeating your reminder phrase.

EB = Beginning of the **E**ye**B**row — *This headache*

SE = **S**ide of the **E**ye — *This headache*

UE = **U**nder the **E**ye — *This headache*

UN = **U**nder the **N**ose — *This headache*

Ch = **Ch**in — *This headache*

CB = Beginning of the **C**ollar**B**one — *This headache*

UA = **U**nder the **A**rm — *This headache*

BN = **B**elow the **N**ipple — *This headache*

Th = **Th**umb — *This headache*

IF = **I**ndex **F**inger — *This headache*

MF = **M**iddle **F**inger — *This headache*

BF = **B**aby **F**inger — *This headache*

KC = **K**arate **C**hop — *This headache*

9 Gamut Procedure: Tap the Gamut Point while doing the following:

1. Close your eyes.

2. Open your eyes.

3. Eyes hard down right while holding the head steady.

4. Eyes hard down left while holding the head steady.

5. Roll your eyes around in a circle in one direction.

6. Roll your eyes in a circle in the reverse direction.

7. Hum two seconds of a song .

8. Count rapidly from 1 to 5.

9. Hum two seconds of a song again.

Repeat the Sequence: Tap each point while repeating your reminder phrase.

EB = Beginning of the **E**ye**B**row — *This headache*

SE = **S**ide of the **E**ye — *This headache*

UE = Under the **E**ye — *This headache*

UN = Under the **N**ose — *This headache*

Ch = **Ch**in — *This headache*

CB = Beginning of the **C**ollar**B**one — *This headache*

UA = Under the **A**rm — *This headache*

BN = **B**elow the **N**ipple — *This headache*

Th = **Th**umb — *This headache*

IF = **I**ndex **F**inger — *This headache*

MF = **M**iddle **F**inger — *This headache*

BF = **B**aby **F**inger — *This headache*

KC = **K**arate **C**hop — *This headache*

You have now finished a complete round of EFT's Basic Recipe. The next thing to do is evaluate your progress.

How does it feel now? If the headache has completely disappeared, congratulations, you're done. No further treatment is needed. For the purposes of this example, we'll say that the pain has gone down to a 3 or 4. It doesn't hurt as much as it did, but it's still there.

Adjusted Setup: Tap the Karate Chop point or rub the Sore Spot while saying:

> *Even though I still have some of this headache, I fully and completely accept myself.*

> *Even though I still have some of this headache, I fully and completely accept myself.*

> *Even though I still have some of this headache, I fully and completely accept myself.*

The Sequence: Tap each point while repeating your reminder phrase.

- **EB** = Beginning of the **E**ye**B**row —*Remaining headache*

- **SE** = **S**ide of the **E**ye —*Remaining headache*

- **UE** = **U**nder the **E**ye —*Remaining headache*

- **UN** = **U**nder the **N**ose —*Remaining headache*

- **Ch** = **Ch**in —*Remaining headache*

- **CB** = Beginning of the **C**ollar**B**one —*Remaining headache*

- **UA** = **U**nder the **A**rm —*Remaining headache*

- **BN** = **B**elow the **N**ipple —*Remaining headache*

- **Th** = **Th**umb —*Remaining headache*

- **IF** = **I**ndex **F**inger —*Remaining headache*

MF = Middle Finger — *Remaining headache*

BF = Baby Finger — *Remaining headache*

KC = Karate Chop — *Remaining headache*

9 Gamut Procedure: Tap the Gamut Point while doing the following:

1. Close your eyes.
2. Open your eyes.
3. Eyes hard down right while holding the head steady.
4. Eyes hard down left while holding the head steady.
5. Roll your eyes around in a circle in one direction.
6. Roll your eyes in a circle in the reverse direction.
7. Hum two seconds of a song.
8. Count rapidly from 1 to 5.
9. Hum two seconds of a song again.

The Sequence: Tap each point while repeating your reminder phrase.

EB = Beginning of the EyeBrow — *Remaining headache*

SE = Side of the Eye — *Remaining headache*

UE = Under the Eye — *Remaining headache*

UN = Under the Nose — *Remaining headache*

Ch = Chin — *Remaining headache*

CB = Beginning of the CollarBone — *Remaining headache*

UA = Under the Arm — *Remaining headache*

BN = **B**elow the **N**ipple —*Remaining headache*

Th = **Th**umb —*Remaining headache*

IF = **I**ndex **F**inger —*Remaining headache*

MF = **M**iddle **F**inger —*Remaining headache*

BF = **B**aby **F**inger —*Remaining headache*

KC = **K**arate **C**hop —*Remaining headache*

You have now completed an entire EFT treatment for headache pain. You will use the same procedure to apply EFT's Basic Recipe to any problem.

The Apex Effect

As you practice EFT and show others how to use it, you'll hear all kinds of explanations as to how or why it works.

We use the term "Apex affect," which was coined by Dr. Roger Callahan, to describe these explanations. They all indicate the clients' propensity to explain away their obvious relief. To some people, it is just not believable that tapping could produce these results, so they attempt to explain the improvements by other means. Clients say that the problem went away because they *"can't think about it any more."* Upon investigation, however, it is discovered that they can, indeed, recount the formerly traumatic incident in great detail. What they really mean is that they can't think about the problem *in the same way* as before.

Sometimes they say, "All that tapping confused me," or, "The tapping is a distraction." Or a client will say, "All those years of previous therapy finally worked for me." They achieve relief immediately after or during tapping but, to them, tapping couldn't have been the true cause of their new freedom. Why? Because it doesn't "compute" or match their belief systems. So they conclude that the results must have come from "real therapy" (talk therapy, etc.) and somehow, as if by magic, all that previous emotional work chose this moment to become effective. This is nonsensical, of course, but some people would rather believe such explanations than to give any credit to the tapping. A comedy writer would find great material here.

In some cases, the client honesty doesn't remember how distressed, uncomfortable, anxious, stressed, or in pain he or she was at the beginning of an EFT session. Keeping track of the person's "before" picture, complete with its rating on the intensity scale, helps keep things in perspective.

In the end, though, it doesn't matter who or what gets the credit. What matters is that the person feels better. That's what EFT is all about.

One thing I can say with confidence is that it is just about impossible to do EFT incorrectly. People have gotten excellent results when tapping on "wrong" EFT points, by omitting or forgetting some points, by tapping on a single point rather than the entire sequence, by tapping on the points upside down, or by tapping entirely mentally, without touching the points. They have completely changed the Setup so it bears little or no resemblance to the Setup I just taught you. They have turned EFT on its head, and it still worked. I will remind you again that the Basic Recipe is simply a starting place and that, once you understand it, you can experiment with EFT variations to your heart's content—and with my blessing.

3

The Acceptance Phrase

The first element of every EFT Setup is a statement about the problem. But just as important is the second part, which is the Acceptance Phrase. The combined statement says that even though I have this problem, I accept myself. The Acceptance Phrase is an affirmation, which I consider crucial to the effectiveness of EFT.

But for many who try EFT, the Setup is a stumbling block. In a typical workshop of several hundred people, as many as half feel uncomfortable saying, "I fully and completely accept myself." For some the incongruity is so severe that they literally can't speak.

EFT can help anyone resolve old emotional issues that contribute to low self-esteem or feelings of guilt or shame, but for now, if the Setup is a problem for you or your client, try saying one of the following statements while you tap:

Even though I can't yet fully and completely accept myself, I would like to some day fully and completely accept myself.

Even though I can't quite fully and completely accept myself, I'll be okay.

Even though it's hard for me to say that I fully and completely accept myself, I can let go of that for now and do this work.

Even though I don't yet accept myself, I can and do acknowledge myself.

If the acceptance phrase causes intense emotional pain or discomfort, or if it feels totally untrue, try changing the Setup altogether to something like:

Even though I have this _____, I would like to feel better.

Even though I have this feeling of sadness, I can enjoy life.

Even though I have this tightness in my stomach, I can relax.

Even though I have this anger and frustration, it's going away.

Even though I'm worried and don't know what to expect, I choose peace.

As you experiment with Setups, try different variations. For example, try saying,

Even though I feel _____, I absolutely do accept myself.

Even though I feel very upset, I would like to love and forgive myself.

Even though I feel guilty about what happened, I forgive myself and anyone and anything that contributed in any way to this feeling.

Setups, by the way, can be of any length. While tapping on the Karate Chop point or massaging the Sore Spot, say whatever you like about the problem. You can also talk *to* the problem. The more detailed, specific, colorful, and interesting your Setup, the more likely you are to experience good results. As you read examples of how people have worked with EFT throughout this book, you'll begin to appreciate the important role that imagination and intuition play in this process. Be ready to let your own imagination and intuition work on your behalf as you start tapping.

Here are some recommendations from EFT practitioner Betty Moore-Hafter for softening the delivery of EFT's Acceptance Phrase. Her approach is ideal for those who need to tiptoe into their issues, which includes a good percentage of the PTSD population. Try any of these Acceptance Phrases on yourself and on others, and experiment with your own variations. Beginning with the right Setup is part of the "art of delivery," saving considerable time and discomfort in EFT sessions for complex problems.

Soft Language to
Ease the EFT Acceptance Phrase

by Betty Moore-Hafter

As I understand it, the EFT Setup paves the way for healing by shifting the hard, locked-up energy of psychological reversal to the softer energy of self-acceptance. I have found that creative wording can be especially helpful toward this end. Here are some of my favorites:

1. "...with kindness and compassion" or "...without judgment"

These and similar words contribute an extra dimension of support and care, especially when the issue is a sensitive one. Tears often come to people's eyes as we add these simple words.

Even though I feel unworthy, I deeply and completely accept myself with kindness and compassion — it's been hard for me.

Even though I'm so afraid of rejection, I deeply accept myself with gentleness and compassion — I've been hurt a lot.

Even though I feel guilty for that mistake I made, I totally accept myself without judgment. I'm only human.

2. "I want to bring healing to this."

Some people balk at the words "I deeply accept myself" and say, "But I don't accept myself! I hate myself for this." One gentle way to proceed is to say:

Even though I don't accept myself, I can accept that this is just where I am right now. And even though I don't accept myself, I want to bring healing to this. I would like to feel better, find more peace, and reach more self-acceptance.

3. "The truth is…"

These words can usher in powerful reframes. And when you reframe a situation while tapping, it does shift the energy and things begin to change.

Even though I crave this cigarette, the truth is, cigarettes are making me sick.

Even though I still feel guilty, the truth is, I've done nothing wrong. This is false guilt.

Even though I still feel responsible for my sister, the truth is, she is an adult. She's responsible for herself now.

4. "I'm willing to see it differently…"

Sometimes amazing things happen after adding the words, "I'm willing to see it differently." One of my clients was convinced that she could never have a child because she might abandon that child the way her father abandoned her. As we tapped through her pain from the father issue, I began adding the phrase, "and I'm willing to see it differently."

Even though my father really hurt me, I love and accept myself, and I'm willing to see it differently.

After several rounds of tapping, she seemed calm and said thoughtfully, "You know, I think my father really did love me in his own way. That's all he was capable of." She felt at peace with it for the first time. And, when I heard from her later, she and her husband were talking about having children. She knew she was not her father and would do it differently. She saw it all differently.

5.   "That was then and this is now."

When childhood pain is being healed, people often feel great relief when words like these are added.

Even though when I was eight years old, I cried alone and no one came. I deeply love and accept my young self. And that was then and this is now. Now I have lots of help and support.

Even though I still feel anxious, afraid that something bad will happen. I deeply accept myself. And even though my child self felt anxious all the time, afraid my father would explode, I love and accept that child self. That was then and this is now. Now I'm safe. I don't need this hyper-vigilance anymore. I can relax now.

6.   "I'm open to the possibility…"

"Choice" statements are of course very empowering when we are ready for them. But sometimes stating a choice is too much of a stretch. Often, the gentlest way to introduce a better choice is to simply bring in the idea of possibility.

Even though I'm full of doubt that I can lose weight, I deeply accept myself and I'm open to the possibility that it may be easier than I think.

Even though I'm stuck in this anger and don't want to let it go, I'm open to the possibility that it would be nice to feel more peaceful about this.

Even though I don't think EFT will work for me, I deeply accept myself and I'm willing to entertain the possibility that maybe EFT will help. I'm ready for some help.

I believe that when we open the door of possibility just a crack, it is enough to start the healing process into motion.

With all of these phrases, you can keep "I deeply and completely accept myself" and add the extra phrase, or you can substitute the phrase. Experiment and see what works for you!

※ ※ ※

And there are more variations. Instead of saying, "I completely and fully accept myself," you can simply say:

I'm okay.   *I'll be okay.*

I'll feel better soon.   *Everything's improving*

Or something similar. This, by the way, is how we use EFT with children. The phrase "I fully and completely accept myself" makes little sense to kids. Instead, a child who's upset can say something like the following:

Even though I flunked the math test, I'm a cool kid, I'm okay.

Even though I lost my backpack and I'm mad at myself, I'm still an awesome kid.

More Notes on Positive Setups

In addition to adding Acceptance Phrases that help the user feel relaxed and confident, you can improve the effectiveness of Setups by adding a phrase or two that reinforces positive results.

EFT practitioner Angela Treat Lyon says, "I also use the phrase *'BECAUSE I love and accept myself,'* which I start as soon as it's apparent that the person has shifted to make new choices. This is very empowering. And lately I've been using *'because I love and BELIEVE in myself,'* which is also really powerful."

Dr. Phillip Mountrose and Dr. Jane Mountrose use what they call a "Miracle Reframe," in which they add the phrase "Anything is possible and miracles are happening now" to the Setup:

Even though I have this _____, I know that anything is possible and miracles are happening now.

As they explain, improvements occur rapidly when we align ourselves with "higher vibrations."

Another way to make Setups more positive is to use Dr. Patricia Carrington's "Choices" phrasing, which she explains in Chapter Eight.

With EFT, you can tap a problem out, and with the same basic technique, you can tap a solution in. Nothing is more versatile than that! No matter how you phrase your Setup, tapping on your EFT points will help, but tapping on both "problem" and "solution" phrases will help bring about long-lasting positive changes in record time.

4

Tapping for PTSD

To apply EFT's Basic Recipe to Post-Traumatic Stress Disorder, you can begin with any physical symptom or anything the person wants to focus on, but an excellent way to start is with a general statement that does not involve a specific memory or event.

Those who have already studied EFT know that this goes against my advice to begin with specific events rather than vague or general statements. However, treating trauma cases can be very different from using EFT to help someone lose weight, fix a sore back, or improve a golf game. Because the events that trigger PTSD can be so intense, tiptoeing up on them, approaching them gently and gradually, and starting with vague, general, or "global" statements, can be an excellent idea. This has the advantage of "taking the edge off" the problem so that deeper work can be done with much less emotional pain

If you are an experienced practitioner already familiar with PTSD, starting with a specific intrusive memory can be the fastest way to clear both the memory and all of the problems associated with it, but this may cause acute discomfort and an increase in PTSD symptoms. Throughout this book, you will find examples of both approaches. I present the "general description" Setup first because I consider it relatively safe as well as effective, and I encourage anyone who is new to EFT or to PTSD to try it first.

Example of the Basic Recipe Applied to a General Description

The following example Setups introduce EFT gently by working around a problem rather than confronting it head-on. Note that it does not describe what happened. This type of Setup is recommended for anyone who does not feel ready to focus on a traumatic event, who seems overcome with emotion, or who is highly skeptical and does not yet feel a sense of rapport with his or her practitioner or instructor.

Try starting with one of these Setups, or create something similar. The following examples all end with, "I fully and completely accept myself."

Setup (tap the KC Point or massage the Sore Spot):

Even though I feel overwhelmed, I fully and completely accept myself.

Even though I don't expect this tapping business to help me at all...

Even though I don't want to think about what went on over there…

Even though I'm afraid to try something new…

Even though I've already tried everything and have been disappointed…

Even though I feel discouraged…

Even though nothing has helped me get my old life back…

Say the Setup three times.

The Sequence (Tap the EFT points from head to hands):

While tapping the EFT points in sequence, say an appropriate reminder phrase, such as:

Don't want to think… Don't want to think… Don't want to think…

Overwhelmed… Overwhelmed… Overwhelmed…

Nothing helps… Nothing helps… Nothing helps…

9-Gamut Treatment: While tapping the Gamut Point, close your eyes, open your eyes, look down hard right, look down hard left, roll your eyes in one direction, roll them in the opposite direction, hum a tune, count from 1 to 5, and hum a tune.

Repeat the Sequence, saying the reminder phrase. Often after a full round of tapping for a general Setup, the person feels calmer and more comfortable.

At this point, you can repeat the entire round of EFT tapping for the same general Setup or you can switch topics or use a different Setup for the same general theme.

By starting with a general theme or a nonspecific statement, you introduce EFT gently, giving the person time to get used to the procedure and experience its results before going on to more serious issues.

If you suffer from PTSD yourself, general statements are an excellent way to begin because they build a foundation of balanced energy, which prepares you energetically so that when you do address specific memories, you'll be more prepared, you'll feel more comfortable, and your results will be more effective. For more detailed do-it-yourself instructions, see Chapter Thirteen.

Example of the Basic Recipe
Applied to a Specific Memory

In this next example, the person is haunted by a powerful explosion and feels ready to talk about it. We start by asking the person to measure his or her discomfort on a scale from 0 to 10.

Measure Intensity. Measure from 0 to 10 on the Intensity Scale.

Setup (tap the KC Point or massage the Sore Spot):

Even though I have this recurring flashback to the moment of the explosion, I fully and completely accept myself.

Even though I have this recurring flashback to the moment of the explosion, I fully and completely accept myself.

Even though I have this recurring flashback to the moment of the explosion, I fully and completely accept myself.

The Sequence (EFT points from head to hands):

Explosion. Explosion. Explosion. Explosion…

9-Gamut Treatment: While tapping the Gamut Point, close your eyes, open your eyes, look down hard right, look down hard left, roll your eyes in one direction, roll them in the opposite direction, hum a tune, count from 1 to 5, and hum a tune.

Repeat the Sequence:

Explosion. Explosion. Explosion. Explosion…

Measure Intensity. If the level has gone down to zero, the person will be able to remember and talk about this event without being distressed. It no longer triggers emotional intensity.

If the person feels better but is still a little upset or uncomfortable, start over using this Setup:

Even though I still have some of this recurring flashback to the moment of the explosion, I fully and completely accept myself.

And for the tapping sequence use the Reminder Phrase:

Remaining recurring explosion… Remaining recurring explosion… Remaining recurring explosion…

As long as the person continues to feel better, this protocol can be repeated several times. When the person feels emotionally neutral (the discomfort level has fallen to zero), this Setup has served its purpose and you can move on.

When thinking about the explosion in a general way no longer generates an emotional response, you can ask the person to describe the event—where it happened, what the person was doing, what day it was, what time it was, what the person saw, heard, smelled, felt, etc. If any of these questions or recollections make the person uncomfortable, go back a step and start tapping with a new Setup for that specific aspect of the event.

In fact, it helps to have the person continue to tap the EFT points while talking. The easiest way to do this is to continue tapping yourself and ask the person to mirror your motions while your conversation continues. This tapping does not involve a Setup or any reminder phrases, but it serves an important purpose by releasing energy blocks and maintaining the person's energy balance throughout the conversation.

❊ ❊ ❊

Dr. Carol Look makes an important point when she observes that most of us, if not all of us, have at least a few traumatic memories and that a key to successfully treating just about any problem or symptom may be to find and neutralize those memories. She also reminds us that PTSD symptoms are often overlooked, ignored, or misdiagnosed.

How Unresolved Trauma Triggers PTSD

by Dr. Carol Look

Post-Traumatic Stress Disorder doesn't have just one single identifying symptom—it has several, and they can seem contradictory. For example, if you have PTSD, you might appear depressed and apathetic, or you might feel anxious and be hyper-vigilant. Your symptoms might be chronic, accumulating over many years of repeated trauma, or they might stem from a single event such as a major car accident. Not everyone experiences flashbacks and dissociation or other well-known PTSD symptoms. Because there is so much confusion about PTSD, I believe this prevalent disorder is greatly under-diagnosed. The more I learn about PTSD, the more I am convinced that it is the underlying cause of the majority of physical health challenges and emotional issues we face today.

A distressing event is categorized as a "trauma" when we experience two features—both a threat to our survival and extreme helplessness. When you experience a trauma, your system actually "freezes" because the terror is too overwhelming to process in that moment. In essence, what the trauma specialists tell us is that during this "freeze response" we download and encode the traumatic memory into our body, cutting off any conscious awareness of these sensory memories. Symptoms of PTSD are the result of incomplete processing of any event we have perceived as traumatic. The "freeze response" never gets discharged. Two results are inevitable: (1) these sensations—sights, sounds and smells—are stored in our body's memory and (2) they will resurface at a later time. Because intense terror interferes with normal brain processing, the very nature of experiencing a trauma cuts off our access to the critical emotional and physical process we need to experience in order to discharge the trauma and prevent the later emergence of PTSD.

When the unexpressed terror and bodily sensations resurface later in life, it is common to become stuck in an endless cycle of frightening thoughts and memories that mimic the actual event as if you are reliving it. So when you are deprived of an opportunity to discharge the emotional and physical repercussions of the original trauma, the unresolved feelings are expressed through flashbacks, intense arousal, avoidance, or other problematic emotions on a daily basis.

Because PTSD symptoms can be difficult to identify, people who turn to therapists for help are often misunderstood. If someone schedules a therapy session to quit smoking, most practitioners focus on cigarette cravings and don't explore past traumatic events. Working for years with addictions and substance abuse taught me to look for old traumas under every addiction.

People who live through traumatic events typically disconnect or dissociate from their emotions as a survival mechanism, but most therapists haven't been trained to understand this complex mechanism.

To be clinically successful, it's essential to understand that anxiety, apathy, or even alcohol and drug use are forms of self-medication for the purpose of self-protection, a way of dealing with unprocessed emotions. This self-protecting pattern in the face of trauma leads later to the symptom cluster we now refer to as PTSD.

In some of the cases I treated after the 9/11 attack, clients caught in downtown New York were able to describe the route they took to escape, what they had been wearing, and what they saw, but it wasn't until after using EFT on their incomplete memories and bodily sensations that the full story unfolded. One woman said to me, *"I can't believe it, I can hear it now!"* Her recollection of the events had been silent until the EFT allowed her to reintegrate all of her senses.

The same lack of integration can happen as a result of car accidents. The victims can remember and recite everything they saw with vivid accuracy. But until they use EFT on the pieces of memory they have from the accident, they might not be able to recall the screeching brakes or the smell of burning rubber.

Remember, a major feature of trauma is the distortion of memory that occurs as a safety mechanism to protect us from being overwhelmed. Once you and the client have tapped and successfully discharged the "freeze response" from the trauma, the client can see the entire picture and is therefore no longer haunted by fears about his or her current safety. When the client can tell the story from start to finish without interruption, feeling completely calm and neutral, you know the session has been a success and the traumatic memory has been neutralized with EFT. You can verify that the results are permanent by checking with the client at a later date. For example, the woman who could suddenly hear the sounds of the World Trade Center collapsing and her colleagues screaming, stopped having nightmares and flashbacks. These are results I have come to expect with EFT.

Insomnia is a very common problem with Post-Traumatic Stress. When clients contact a health care practitioner complaining that they're sleep-deprived or having trouble falling or staying asleep, taking a complete history is vital. While each case of insomnia is different, it is useful to check to see if it is as a result of PTSD or early childhood trauma. Again, using EFT for the available pieces of traumatic memories will reintegrate the memories, discharge the freeze response, and remove any "need" for PTSD symptoms such as hyper-vigilance or the startle response, both of which interfere with normal sleeping habits.

For some individuals, getting a divorce or getting fired might be as traumatic as an event such as 9/11 is to others. Counselors never know what registers as "traumatic" to each individual. PTSD is always in the back of my mind when I work with new clients, and the question I routinely ask when someone begins to describe a symptom or problem is, *"When did it start?"* I'll also ask clients open-ended questions about their habitual thoughts. I'll often ask questions about their responses to environmental cues such as, *"Are you sensitive to loud noises or bright lights?"*

There is frequently a lag time between the occurrence of a traumatic event and the resulting physical or emotional symptoms. I've heard people say, *"The accident was six months before my symptoms started, so there can't be a connection."* In truth, the accident could have taken place a year before the symptoms started, or even decades before the onset of an illness, and still be the cause.

At the veterans' conference in San Francisco, I worked with two men whose physical symptoms had gotten worse as a result of PTSD. Carlin, then 26, had inherited a family condition, a tremor in his hand, that intensified when he returned home from Iraq. When he tried EFT, the tremor dramatically decreased and he has since enjoyed periods of remission. He later taught EFT to his sister, who also inherited this symptom, and her tremor decreased as well.

Art, who served in Vietnam, had tinnitus, or ringing in the ears, that would vary greatly in volume throughout the day. He soon realized that this symptom was a kind of barometer that reflected his emotional state. When he focused on a positive feeling or memory, the ringing subsided, and when he focused on a stressful memory, it became more annoying, even insistent.

Like most combat veterans, these two men felt compelled to be "machines" out on the battlefield. If you have been trained to take orders and act like a machine, you have no choice but to ignore your gut instincts and your emotions. These men were trained to take and give orders in a robotic fashion, which required that they disconnect themselves from their feelings. It's not that they weren't afraid or horrified, it's that the new commands overrode these instincts to run, hide, or protect themselves. This is an alarmingly fast way to create Post-Traumatic Stress Disorder because when you are disconnected from your emotions, you become desensitized to your body's intelligence and your mind's intuition. The thinking brain goes off-line and you adapt by developing an unnatural ability to go on auto-pilot, ready to shoot anything that moves. Every situation becomes life or death, and you have no time to do anything but react. Imagine what a tightrope these veterans walk when they try to resume civilian life.

In addition, many veterans suffer from shame and guilt over what they did during the wars. They might experience chronic pain or other physical symptoms as a result of an unconscious conviction that they don't deserve to be happy and joyful. One veteran said to me that he had made other families miserable by killing people, so he certainly didn't deserve success in his own life. People who are consumed with guilt on a psychological level find unconscious ways and reasons to punish themselves. EFT practitioners need to look past the punishing behavior and assess the origins of the guilt. Even though guilt and shame may not fall neatly into the category of Post-Traumatic Stress Disorder, they are chronic feelings that some PTSD victims suffer from that naturally lead to self sabotage and limitations.

The repeated traumatic memories that Carlin and Art tried but failed to control responded extremely well to EFT.

Art suffered from survivor's guilt because numerous explosions that were meant for him killed his fellow officers instead. His guilt ate away at him for decades. When he wasn't feeling overwhelmed with guilt, he was overreacting to everyday incidents in a state of panic. He had spent 30 years screaming orders at his wife, as though *"Take out the garbage!"* was a matter of life or death. To him, at those times, it seemed to be.

Art's wife suffered from PTSD as a result of living with an angry, over-reactive man suffering from extreme and untreated PTSD. She too was enrolled in the veterans' study and made significant emotional and physical improvement. Art continued to make steady improvement during the retreat. He began walking better, enjoyed sleeping more, and noticed feeling optimistic for the first time in decades. After two couples sessions, instead of being isolated, angry, and threatened by each other, Art and his wife were thrilled that they were actually talking again.

Carlin had numerous memories about the most gruesome events I had ever heard described. By the time he was 22, he had already completed two tours of duty in Iraq. He felt he could never relax and thought he needed to sleep with one eye open. Chronic danger affected his entire system, leaving him anxious, nervous, and desperate to escape through alcohol and cigarettes. These feelings and symptoms naturally interfered with his sleep and gave him horrific nightmares. To stop the nightmares and prevent him from waking in the middle of the night, he drank excessive amounts of alcohol.

Carlin experienced profound emotional improvement the very first day of the veterans' retreat after we collapsed two of his most threatening and haunting war memories, which included sights, smells, and sounds. In one experience, a small child with a bomb strapped to his chest exploded ten feet in front of Carlin. This was something Carlin thought he would be condemned to live with forever. With EFT, we neutralized all the pieces of this memory until telling the entire story no longer triggered any emotional charge in his body and mind. His stunned reaction was, *"Huh... That's weird..."* At first he had trouble believing the change.

We tested whether EFT had worked thoroughly by asking Carlin to repeat the title he gave to this "movie" or specific event, *"The Child Blows Up and It's All Over Me."* He walked through the details of the story out loud. He was able to repeat each gruesome detail of the event in a completely neutral tone of voice because it no longer had any emotional impact for him. While it was obviously something he would rather not have experienced, it no longer haunted him on a daily basis. His mind and body didn't need to relive the terrible details as though it was happening repeatedly in the present moment, because EFT had allowed him to process the terror and discharge the "frozen" pieces of the trauma.

The second movie title Carlin chose for a traumatic memory from his tour in Iraq was *"Iraqis in the Grass."* He and some fellow officers were moving through a field of tall grass thinking they were safe from enemy fire. After stepping over a hill, Carlin was suddenly looking down the barrel of an enemy gun, and the panic he felt completely flooded his system. Someone behind him saved his life by shooting the enemy soldier, but the fear, life-threatening panic, and trauma of the moment stayed with him for over four years until the veterans' retreat. We again collapsed each aspect of this specific event using Gary Craig's "Movie Technique," until Carlin was able to say, *"Iraqis in the Grass... That one doesn't bother me anymore either."*

In an hour and a half, this young man went from being totally withdrawn with a stone-faced stare to an open, friendly young guy able to relate and talk to everyone at the retreat. That first night Carlin only had one drink and one cigarette with his friends, and then he slept through the night without any nightmares – an incredible improvement for him. In the days ahead we kept working on his war memories with EFT, and he continued to improve emotionally and physically. When he returned home, he had a short-term relapse and started drinking again in response to unresolved feelings around his friendships and his father. These challenges had nothing to do with the war or the war memories we had neutralized. The war memories no longer haunted him, in spite of all the tragedy he witnessed. Carlin continues to use EFT and has been enthusiastically introducing EFT to other veterans in his area as well as to family members.

How is it that EFT can be so effective so quickly? And how can its results last so long? I believe that with EFT we are rewiring or re-integrating the person's sensory memories and traumas so they are no longer compartmentalized into small fragments that haunt and threaten the person. EFT allows us to discharge the original and once useful and protective "freeze response" so that pieces of the trauma no longer take up valuable emotional energy. Once the memories and sensations from the trauma are integrated fully into consciousness by using EFT, the client no longer needs to be hyper-vigilant to protect from the next possible attack. The trauma has been processed fully, on all levels, leaving room for normal everyday thoughts and activities.

The counselor's primary job is to help PTSD clients feel safe. Unfortunately, well-meaning counselors often frighten their clients by charging in with EFT prematurely. I recommend that practitioners working with PTSD clients introduce EFT with setup statements that focus on physical symptoms or a general feeling of stress or anxiety rather than specific events or traumatic memories. This will help the client get a feel for the EFT process while experiencing some of its benefits, all as part of laying the foundation for the later deeper work.

Once you have gained some rapport with the client (which is often difficult with PTSD clients) and he or she has become accustomed to tapping and talking, I recommend identifying specific events and using the *Tell The Story Technique* or the *Movie Technique* as much as possible. A simple question such as *"Can you tell me about the memory that won't go away?"* is also very effective.

If the client is unable or reluctant to identify a specific trigger or memory, it can be useful to remain more emotionally distant with Setup Phrases such as:

> *Even though I can't go there yet, I fully and completely accept myself.*

> *Even though something terrifying happened, I deeply and completely accept myself.*

Working with PTSD clients requires intense attention from the counselor. While clients are recounting one of their stories, instruct them to tap for the intensity the instant you see facial expressions change, notice muscles become tense, or hear their voice crack or stop altogether. Timing is everything, and we don't want to inadvertently re-traumatize someone who's contacted us for help.

After using EFT on several aspects of a traumatic memory, it is critical that you "test" your work to make sure the EFT was effective. Ask the client to tell the story again from start to finish. Does the client feel and act emotionally neutral throughout every part of the story? Can he or she look at any detail or sub-plot without feeling stressed or uncomfortable? Has the emotional intensity from that entire experience disappeared? If so, you have successfully erased some of the originating causes of the person's PTSD and the healing journey can begin.

If a symptom does return, it is almost always the result of an incomplete treatment of an original trauma or memory. As Gary taught us, it is likely that another "aspect" of the event has surfaced or been triggered by the person's environment. The new aspects are often easy to identify and target with EFT.

Final thoughts—tread gently, listen deeply, and use compassion liberally. Watch for miniscule signs of distress while working with these clients, and once you have developed rapport, neutralize any and all emotional and physical signs of hidden trauma with EFT. Whatever problem or challenge your client presents to you, the odds are incredibly high that it contains links and echoes to events in the past. Luckily for all of us, EFT is an incredibly efficient tool to neutralize original childhood traumas as well as current symptoms of PTSD.

※ ※ ※

5

EFT for Combat Veterans

As mentioned earlier, I have been fascinated with EFT's profound effects on Post-Traumatic Stress Disorder since my colleague Adrienne Fowlie and I visited a Los Angeles Veterans Administration hospital in August of 1994. Our DVD titled "Six Days at the V.A." shows several veterans being treated on camera.

In each case, we combined the Tell a Story technique with the Tearless Trauma Technique. That is, we invited each veteran to choose an intrusive memory, give it a title, and rate it on the 0-to-10 intensity scale. We would tap until the person felt comfortable enough to start telling the story, and whenever his emotional intensity increased, we would stop the story and tap until the intensity level came back down. Only then would we ask him to resume the story. In most cases the whole procedure took less than five or ten minutes, at the end of which the story teller could recite what happened from beginning to end, often with new details and observations, without any emotional intensity whatsoever.

Those who watch the DVD may notice that Adrienne and I used a slightly different tapping sequence from the one described here and in the *EFT Manual.* This is because in those days we were using a precursor of EFT. The EFT tapping sequence is more streamlined, easier to remember, and just as effective.

Six Days at the V.A.

Our "Six Days at the V.A." video begins with Rich, who had over 100 specific intrusive memories that he rated at a 10 on the 0-to-10 intensity scale. In addition, he had a serious height phobia. He had it before he joined the military, and more than 50 parachute jumps made it worse. Because of his fear of falling, he could not use an elevator, go out on a fire escape, or even look over the second-floor railing at a shopping mall. After a few minutes of EFT tapping, a relaxed and comfortable Rich leaned over the railing of a third-floor fire escape and waved to his friends far below. His height anxiety had gone from a 10 to a zero and stayed there.

Rich then recounted three memories from Cambodia, where the Khmer Rouge (the country's ruling party from 1975 to 1979) killed over a million villagers. Rich's most difficult memory involved coming into a village in April 1975 and finding 20 decapitated bodies. They wore black uniforms, their heads were in one pile, their bodies were in another, there was blood all over, the bodies were swollen in the heat, and the stench was overwhelming. Rich re-experienced all of these sights, sounds, and smells whenever he remembered the scene, which was every day.

We tapped with Rich and soon his discomfort fell to a zero.

Another memory that bothered Rich was an eerie scene created by heavy rains. Coming into a village just before sunrise, through the early morning mist and fog, he was horrified to see bodies rising up from a mass grave. The rain had filled the grave and literally lifted the bodies from the ground, like a scene from a science fiction movie.

Rich tapped this memory from a 10 to a zero as well.

Altogether, we worked with Rich on three specific memories and he worked by himself on another three, so when we next met with him, he had removed the emotional intensity of six different troublesome memories. The test was in the story telling, so we asked him to recount these six events again while trying to recapture their previous emotional intensity. All of these terrifying events, which had dominated his waking thoughts and appeared in his nightmares, were now emotionally neutral.

When I asked Rich which of his other 100 intrusive memories he wanted to work on, it was hard for him to find any at all. This is an example of what we call the Generalization Effect. Memories that are linked or connected in any way often collapse together. When the emotional intensity of one of them goes down or disappears, so does the emotional intensity of the others.

I checked with Rich two months after our session, and he reported that his height phobia had permanently disappeared, he had no intrusive memories from the war in Cambodia, and instead of sleeping only four hours per night he now slept seven and felt well rested, relaxed, and comfortable.

Our next volunteer was Ralph, who worked with Adrienne for his memories of going over a cliff in a Jeep that almost landed on him. He was on maneuvers with a 106 Recoilless Rifle Platoon, and the rifle was mounted on a platform on the Jeep.

The problem was that the Jeep had no brakes, which Ralph reported to his commanding officer. The officer ordered him to drive it anyway because they had to get back to the beach. There was a 90-degree turn in the road, and as the top-heavy Jeep began to slide, Ralph knew they were in trouble.

At this point in his story, Ralph's anxiety rose to a 7. Adrienne had him stop and tap until he felt relaxed, at a zero, and then he resumed his story.

When the Jeep went off the cilff, Ralph flew through the air and landed so hard that everyone assumed his back was broken. Fortunately, it wasn't, but he was hospitalized for his injuries. Ralph said that whenever he thought about the Jeep accident, his stomach felt tight and his left shoulder hurt.

He couldn't get over how comfortable he felt thinking about the accident and even talking about it after tapping. "I normally don't ever talk about it," he said, "because it's too painful." He laughed, marveling over his new situation—being able to think about and even describe out loud those long-ago events that had been excruciatingly painful but which no longer triggered any discomfort.

Ralph's desire to quit smoking gave us an opportunity to show him how EFT can stop a craving in its tracks. Many veterans turn to alcohol, tobacco, drugs, or compulsive behaviors as a form of self-medication, and EFT can help break dependencies and addictions. Ralph started with a very strong craving, and I had him hold the unlit cigarette under his nose and really smell it, take a dry drag from it, and hold it in his hand. He really wanted it! But after tapping for a minute or two, the craving grew weak and then disappeared. As Ralph observed, "Now I have a choice. I can have a cigarette or I can tap and let the craving go away."

Anthony, our next veteran, was an out-patient who came to the V.A. hospital for treatment for his fear of crowds and crowded places (hyper-vigilance). He described his anxiety as an "ultra-awareness of harm," developed in Vietnam, which left him always looking over his shoulder and thinking of himself as a target.

Anthony avoided restaurants, but he told us that if he were ever to enter one, he would go straight to the table that would give him the best view of all the entrances and exits, and he would sit with his back to the wall, keeping an eye on everyone, especially those who were coming or going.

Even though Anthony was highly skeptical about EFT, he tapped with us. Totally amazed by his resulting lack of anxiety, he walked with us to a nearby restaurant. Everything was fine until I opened the door and invited him to walk in. His anxiety level rose to a 10 and he stopped in his tracks. This happened because Anthony was tuning into a new or different aspect of his problem. It's not unusual for problems to have many aspects, and as soon as one materializes, we tap it away and go on from there.

In Anthony's case, the thoughts that came to his mind at the restaurant door had nothing to do with lunch or the threat posed by crowds of strangers but rather the grief he felt over the death of his brother. "I couldn't even talk about it before," he said. Now he not only talked about it, he tapped about it, and soon the emotional sting disappeared. He also tapped for the pain he felt over the loss of close friends in Vietnam. "I remember the scenes," he said, "I remember what happened, but it feels different. Something is missing, and I realize that it's grief. The grief is what's missing. There isn't any pain. I can't believe I'm not upset. I don't feel the shock, the sword through my heart, that I've been getting therapy for since 1978."

At the restaurant, Anthony realized that he felt fine, and he walked through the door. To really give EFT a test, he sat in the middle of the room with his back to the entrance and most of the customers. "My awareness was still there," he said, "but in a good way. I no longer saw myself as a target. I really enjoyed myself."

Our next veteran was Robert, who had been in therapy for 30 years for Post-Traumatic Stress Disorder. His most intrusive, intense memory, which he replayed constantly in his mind, was a short mental movie that he called "The Kid."

We started by addressing this memory in a general way, with no specific details. In a few rounds of tapping,

Robert's anxiety about "The Kid" fell in stages from a 10 to a zero. Then I asked him to tell the story, starting right before the main action began and stopping whenever he felt his emotions became intense. We would tap until his stress level fell to a zero and then continue.

Robert said he drove into a village in Vietnam with a driver who wanted to stop at a bar. Robert had misgivings about stopping in the village, but he agreed to stay with the truck. Soon a small child, a boy five or six years of age, started walking around the truck. Robert figured the boy was curious, so he wasn't concerned. After a while, the boy disappeared behind a building, and when he came back, Robert realized that he held a grenade in his hand and that he had pulled the pin.

At this point in his story, Robert's intensity level rose so we stopped and tapped about how "I accept myself even though I have some of this kid emotion."

When he resumed the story, Robert said that the kid kept walking toward him. He told him to go back, get away, but he kept coming. Robert took his rifle and fired a couple of rounds at the boy's feet. This memory made him uncomfortable, so we stopped and tapped again. Robert said that finally he had no choice, it would be him and the truck or the kid, so he shot the boy. "I didn't want to, but I had to," he said. We had Robert tap while saying, "I accept myself even though I shot the kid."

Soon Robert's intensity level fell to zero. "I can see the kid, see him lying there," he said. "I can't believe it. It's always a 10 and now it's a zero. It feels so strange."

I asked Robert to tell us the whole story from the beginning, which he did with no emotional discomfort whatsoever. In the retelling, Robert remembered additional details, such as how when the boy got to within 60 or 70 feet of the truck, Robert could see that his fist was clenched. He assumed the boy was holding a rock and that even if he threw it at Robert he wouldn't do much damage. Then, when the boy was 40 feet away, he could see it was a grenade. He told the boy to leave and then heard the ping that told him the grenade was live and fully armed. He fired at the boy's feet, but he kept coming as though in a trance. Robert shot him in the shoulder, but he still kept coming, walking like a zombie toward the truck. He knew he had to stop him before he reached the truck, so he shot him in the head. The boy fell, the grenade dropped behind him and exploded, and soon people were running out of nearby buildings, yelling and demanding to know why he had shot the child.

These memories normally caused an intense emotional reaction in Robert, but now, he said, "It's like I'm watching a movie." His intensity level remained at a zero. He said he didn't blame the people who accused him because they didn't know what had happened. And he stopped blaming himself as well.

Later, Robert talked about another memory that normally caused him distress, where a whole village was wiped out, but now he yawned. When I asked him how he felt about these old memories, he said he felt bored. He also reported getting his best night's sleep in over five years.

Philip, our next veteran, suffered from severe anxiety headaches. When we started working with him, his headache was at an 8, but it soon fell to a zero and completely disappeared. He said it was like a little miracle.

Philip suffered from a height phobia and the thought of climbing a ladder made him feel jittery, at an 8 or 9 on the intensity scale, and he felt odd sensations in his hands and feet. With five quick rounds of tapping, all of those symptoms disappeared and he was comfortable with heights.

He also suffered from insomnia, even when medicated with sleeping pills. Philip told us that the previous night, he tapped before bed, fell asleep, slept well, and slept through the night without waking up – all without taking any medication.

Gary, our last on-camera veteran, suffered from anxiety and the headaches it produced. Inspired by our group demonstration, he worked on his own to treat a severe headache over his right eye. It moved from his eye to the back of his head, then to the center of his head. Pain moving from one location to another is a common reaction to tapping, and we call it "chasing the pain." When he tapped for the pain in the center of his head, the headache disappeared.

Gary also tapped for the numbness he felt in his fingers, and when that disappeared, he said that he felt so good, he could only describe it as "an exceptional day for me."

We then asked Gary to describe his most intense war memory, which was always at an 8 or 10 because of the guilt he felt over what happened. One night, he and his fellow soldiers shot at enemy troops, but when dawn came, they discovered that the people they had killed were civilians carrying personal possessions, not weapons. The soldiers were instructed to dig a trench and bury the bodies. Gary relived these painful events on an almost daily basis for decades. Now, suddenly, he felt no guilt at all. He could look back, see what happened, and feel completely detached. He could tell the story without being upset. He couldn't get over how different he felt.

Altogether, Adrienne and I worked with veterans, many of them off-camera, to bring over 20 debilitating, traumatic, intrusive memories from a 10 down to zero. None of the sessions lasted longer than 15 minutes. In our follow-up interviews, 80 percent considered the improvements permanent. Their symptoms did not return. For those who did experience a recurrence of symptoms, we recommended a few more rounds of tapping.

In these examples, we went straight for specific traumatic memories and treated them with EFT. This is the same direct approach that I recommend throughout the EFT manual. If the person had several traumatic memories, we started with one, tapped it down to a zero, then moved to the next. Typically, just as we saw with Rich, after a few of these memories have been neutralized, a "generalization effect" collapses the remaining memories so they don't have to be treated individually.

❀ ❀ ❀

At the March 2008 PTSD study in San Francisco, EFT practitioner Sophia Cayer worked with several combat veterans using the same approach that she took with the Gulf War veteran described below. As you read her report, pay particular attention to the gentle and indirect way in which she introduces EFT, defuses intense emotions generated by the Setup, and helps her client find and neutralize core issues.

Layers of Trauma

by Sophia Cayer

John is a Gulf War Veteran in his late thirties, married, with small children. He managed to cope with the side effects of his war experience fairly well until the September 11 event in New York City, which threw him into full-blown PTSD. At that point everything began falling apart.

Situations such as this are far more common than most realize. Delayed reactions are important considerations for anyone working with veterans and their families. Many times veterans arrive home and initially exhibit only minimal or no side effects resulting from their war experiences. Others manage to successfully mask or ignore related emotions. They put up a valiant front, doing their best to resume life as they used to know it. Therefore family and friends think everything is almost back to normal.

Then without warning and for seemingly no reason, things start falling apart. As time goes by even subtle events can spark flashbacks that trigger PTSD symptoms. I have seen veterans triggered while driving because the tire treads on a truck in front of them reminded them of the tires on military vehicles. Video games and newsreels are things they quickly learn to avoid. Major events such as 9/11 or any event they perceive as a threat can trigger flashbacks, intense emotions, physical symptoms, a constant sense of hyper-vigilance, anxiety, sudden unexplainable bursts of anger, nightmares, insomnia, and other PTSD symptoms. Friends and family members can be equally traumatized since they don't understand what is happening. They too need care.

John had been prescribed every available medication believed to help with PTSD symptoms, to no avail. He and his wife had flown all over the country trying various treatments in their search for answers. Less than two months before I met with him, John completed an eight-week PTSD treatment program offered by the V.A. He told me that being among his comrades in itself had offered comfort and he felt a little better while he was at the facility. However, the instant he went home and back into "the real world," his challenges returned. Even with all the medications, he was depressed and lethargic. He spent most of his day slumped in a recliner and couldn't find the motivation to attempt the mental or physical exercises that had been suggested to help his condition. He was exploding at the drop of the hat and found himself constantly arguing with his wife and children.

John was consumed by sadness as well as fear and anger, and he told me that the only reason suicide wasn't an option was that he was too concerned about the pain it would cause his family. He was guilt-ridden about the state of affairs with his family and felt like a failure when it came to military service.

I always make it a point to inquire about the level of anxiety the person feels about even attempting EFT. Most of the time it is a last-ditch effort after a number of disappointing avenues have been explored. Most veterans are not only anxious, they are frightened and uneasy. I tap first on whatever they are feeling, whatever misgivings are there before we go any further. In my experience, this approach opens the door to achieving more profound results in a shorter period of time. It is also a great way to demonstrate how quickly the technique can help them achieve results, which also helps gain their trust and confidence.

When I asked John how he felt about doing this work, he said he was worried, didn't know what to expect, and was disappointed that his wife couldn't be there with him. "She's been here with me most of the time," he said, and I could see emotions and tears beginning to well up.

He said the worst was part was not knowing what to expect. His discomfort level was already at an 8 and he was feeling it in his stomach. He described it as a knot, a tightening up or tension.

Since he was brand new to EFT, I said, "Let me show you how silly it is. Let's just take a crack at it and see how it lands for you and how quickly it can work. If it begins to feel too intense, just let me know.

You don't have to tell anything, just focus the on the tightening up."

KC (Karate Chop) – *Even though I have this anxiety in my stomach, I love and respect myself.*

He couldn't say the words "I love and respect myself" and broke into tears. I assured him he didn't have to say the words and that together we would get through it.

We began again with different words:

KC (Karate Chop) – *Even though I have all this anxiety in my stomach, I choose peace.*

TH (Top of Head) – *All this anxiety.*

EB (Eye Brow) – *All this anxiety.*

SE (Side of Eye) – *All this anxiety.*

UE (Under Eye) – *It is sitting in my stomach.*

UN (Under Nose) – *I don't know what to expect.*

Ch (Chin) – *I have been through enough.*

CB (Collar Bone) – *I just want to feel better.*

UA (Under Arm) – *All this anxiety.*

TH (Top of Head) – *All this fear and anticipation.*

EB (Eye Brow) – *I choose peace.*

SE (Side of Eye) – *This anxiety.*

UE (Under Eye) – *All this tension in my stomach.*

UN (Under Nose) – *This anxiety in my stomach.*

Ch (Chin) – *I choose peace.*

Sensing a major change in his demeanor and voice, I asked him to relax, breathe, and let me know how his stomach was feeling.

He seemed a little surprised when he announced, *"Better — I am probably at a 3 or 4. That is pretty neat!"*

I encouraged him by reminding him that with this wonderful self-empowerment tool, he could soon feel comfortable working on his own, dealing with things as they came up. I also reminded him that he could tap preemptively. The realization that he could be in charge and in control of his emotions as he worked through issues on his own was an empowering thought, one that encouraged the healing process.

KC – *Even though I still have some of this anticipation in my stomach, I choose peace.*

Even though I still have some anticipation in my stomach, and I am not sure what to expect, I choose peace anyway.

TH – *This remaining tightness in my stomach.*

EB – *This remaining tightness.*

SE – *This anticipation in my stomach.*

UE – *I don't know what to expect.*

UN – *This anticipation.*

Ch – *Something else to try.*

CB – *I don't know what to expect.*

UA – *But I choose peace anyway.*

TH – *This anticipation.*

EB – *I choose to feel better.*

SE – *I choose to let go of all this anticipation.*

UE – *And to have peace within.*

At this point he reported his stomach felt better and he felt he was probably down to 1 or zero. "Just a tiny little bit" remained.

TH – *This tiny little bit.*

EB – *That is still sitting in my stomach.*

SE – *I choose peace.*

UE – *I choose peace.*

UN – *This tiny little bit.*

Ch – *Still sitting in my stomach.*

CB – *I choose to believe in me.*

At this point the stomach tightness was gone and he felt ready to proceed. As we continued to work on the more intense and complex issues together, he began to see how EFT might help him get through the days more easily.

It is important to encourage persistence when people will be working on their own, so that they realize there is no need to feel discouraged if they happen to experience intensities going up and down or find themselves switching from one aspect of the problem to another.

Now that John was feeling more relaxed and comfortable knowing what to expect, it was time to move forward.

Based on John's vacant expression when he arrived, which is typical of those severely affected by PTSD, and his rapid shifts from no apparent emotion to high emotion, I knew it was particularly important to be mindful and cautious as we moved forward. I realized that he could experience difficulty in getting to core issues because they were blocked, or he could find that some memories were easily triggered. These are important considerations if you are new to dealing with PTSD.

When I inquired as to what he felt was his most pressing issue, he said it was his depression and anger, but he could offer little else. With a little gentle probing on my part he recalled that the onset occurred in 2000 or 2001, but he still couldn't connect it with anything specific.

Knowing there had been issues with being in and out of the service, I asked John where things stood with his military career. He told me that he wasn't connected any longer with the military. He had left in 1998 and the doctors believed that his PTSD was set off by the events of September 11, 2001. He attempted to re-enter the military following 9/11 and was denied due to his physical condition.

I could hear the emotion in his voice so I immediately interrupted to ask what he was feeling as he relayed the story. His one word answer: *"Anger."*

In an attempt to be more specific, I asked, *"Anger with the government or anger about them not letting you re-enlist?"*

John replied, *"Both. Anger at 9/11 and anger that I couldn't do anything about it."*

I could feel and sense a lot more than anger and quickly received John's confirmation of deep sadness. We tapped for:

KC – *Even though I am filled with all this anger and sadness—there was nothing I could do, they wouldn't even let me try—I am okay anyway.*

Even though I am filled with all this sadness and anger, I wanted to help and there was nothing I could do. I choose peace anyway.

TH – *All this anger and sadness.*

EB – *I am absolutely furious.*

SE – *They wouldn't let me help.*

UE – *They wouldn't let me help.*

UN – *All this grief and sadness.*

Ch – *I am absolutely furious!*

CB – *Why did this have to happen?*

UA – *It just wasn't right.*

TH – *I am angry with the government.*

EB – *They stopped me.*

SE – *I am really furious.*

UE – *I wanted to help.*

UN – *And they wouldn't let me.*

Ch – *They told me no.*

CB – *All this anger and sadness.*

UA – *All this grief and sadness.*
TH – *This grief and sadness.*

We had taken the edge off, but it was obvious that related issues and aspects were bubbling up. Since he was having difficulty voicing anything, I asked, "Did you lose someone close to you in 9/11?"

John said, "No, but I dealt with a lot of dead in the first Gulf war." I could feel a myriad of emotions emanating and knew his mind was racing from event to event and feeling to feeling. We managed to determine that the most predominant feelings were related to rejection by the military.

To help find a core issue, an important underlying event or memory that would bring John's attention from the vague and general to the specific and detailed, I began asking questions related to when and how he learned that he could not rejoin the military. Was it over the phone, in person, or in a letter?

"It was done by computer," he said. "They opened a site taking back prior enlisted. I filled out the paperwork and got rejected. They told me I had too many problems and wasn't medically able, even though I did 8½ years with a screwed-up back that got injured in service."

When I asked, "Does that make you angry?" his voice rose through a swell of emotion and tears until he was almost screaming, "I'm not really angry at the government—I love my government. I would fight and die for my country. I don't know who I am angry at."

I said, "It doesn't matter... You don't have to know..." It was impossible and unnecessary to attempt to sort anything out, so we simply began tapping:

KC – *Even though I am angry and sad at the same time and I am not even sure what this is all about, I am okay.*

Even though I am angry and sad that they rejected me, I am okay.

TH – *That news that came through the computer.*

EB – *They rejected me.*

SE – *I really wanted to go.*

UE – *I wanted to do my duty.*

UN – *I wanted to be there.*

Ch – *They told me no.*

CB – *All these emotions.*

UA – *All this anger and sadness.*

TH – *They told me no.*

EB – *They wouldn't take me even after all I had done.*

SE – *They wouldn't take me.*

UE – *All this rejection.*

UN – *All this sadness and anger that I really don't understand.*

Ch – *This sadness and anger.*

CB – *They said no.*

UA – *This sadness and anger.*

TH – *I saw it in the computer.*

EB – *They said no.*

SE – *All this anger and sadness.*

UE – *This deep anger and sadness.*

UN – *All this frustration.*

CB – *Deep sadness and anger.*

UA – *All this deep sadness.*

John felt the intensity had dropped from a 10 to a 5. It is important to note that many major shifts in intensity are quite common in this situation. Frequently this happens because it is impossible for PTSD victims to remain focused on one aspect of an issue, or even one issue.

I asked, "Which feels more intense, the anger or the sadness?" He replied, "Both feel about the same."

He now felt he might be able to remain focused on receiving the news. Disappointment and despair were intensifying.

KC – *Even though I'm still at a 5, I've still got this anger and disappointment and all this deep sadness, I choose peace.*

Even though I have all this deep sadness and all this anger because they said no, I am okay anyway. I choose peace.

Even though I have all this deep sadness and all this anger because they said no, I am okay anyway. I choose peace.

TH – *All this remaining anger and sadness.*

EB – *This feeling of despair.*

SE – *They wouldn't take me back.*

UE – *All this anger and despair.*

UN – *This deep sadness.*

Ch – *I couldn't believe that news.*

CB – *I didn't want to hear that news.*

UA – *All this anger and sadness.*

TH – *I am still carrying it.*

EB – *This anger and sadness.*

SE – *They said no.*

UN – *This remaining anger and sadness.*

Ch – *Remaining anger sadness.*

I stopped at this point because I could sense a marked improvement. John reported feeling "Relaxed...and I'd say I am at a zero." It was time to test. I asked him to picture himself in front of the computer getting news and see how it felt.

John said he could see himself there with his brother, and as he began to tell me about reading it on the screen, I could sense his emotions on the rise.

I asked, "What does it feel like now?" He replied, "It is just the rejection that hurts." He felt it was at a 3 or 4, and he was feeling it in his chest and stomach.

KC – *Even though I still have this sense of rejection in my chest and stomach, I choose peace. I choose to believe in me.*

Even though I feel this rejection in my chest and stomach, I choose peace, I choose to believe in me.

TH – *This rejection.*

EB – *I couldn't believe that letter.*

SE – *That terrible letter.*

UE – *That rejection.*

UN – *Those rejection words.*

Ch – *It still hurts.*

CB – *It still hurts.*

UA – *All that rejection.*

IW – *All that rejection.*

OW – *They rejected me.*

9G – *They rejected me.*

IW – *All this rejection.*

OW – *I choose to believe in me.*

In the tapping sequence above, I included two optional tapping points, the Inside Wrist (IW) and Outside Wrist (OW), plus the 9 Gamut treatment (9G).

John returned to the computer screen in his mind's eye to read his rejection letter again. This time he reported it was just another screen. He was quite pleased that EFT was working and said that now he had "calmed down big time…"

He felt better equipped to begin dealing with some of traumatic events, so we attempted to gently approach the most haunting ones. It is important to remember that even when someone begins to experience relief, his or her enthusiasm may lead both of you to believe it is time to forge full speed ahead. Please continue to approach things in a gentle and subtle manner. That euphoria and the return of the "I can handle it!" feeling may prove to be short lived, and in a matter of minutes other events will evoke new rivers of emotion.

While it is best if you can "sneak up" on events, these events may continually replay in the person's mind. John reported that many of the scenes came to him like a movie screen that started in the morning and ran all day long. "If something happens in the house," he said, "I explode for no reason at all. I am already fired up. They've got me on all of this crap [medications] that's supposed to help, but nothing works…"

I reminded him that he had a new 'secret weapon' and that it was possible for him to have more than temporary relief.

At this point I thought we would set to work on the non-stop movies. Well, that's not the way it went. We started down that path, but as we worked it led us in different directions. Remember that these are complex cases and it is important to follow and not lead, letting the person work through events and memories as they present themselves. The following will clearly demonstrate how winding the trail can become and how essential it is to let things unfold on their own.

Out of concern about triggering those reading this book, I am offering limited details but the general drift of the tuning-into-events conversation started when John said, " I dealt with something in the Gulf War. It was the scariest thing I ever did in my life, something we never practiced before…"

Again a myriad of emotions were before us, but the most intense was his sense of guilt, the feeling that he had failed to complete his mission according to the rules.

KC – *Even though I am feeling guilty — I feel like a failure as a _____.*

[He couldn't say the words and tears and emotions intensified. Realizing that 'failure' was the trigger and knowing he was more than tuned in, I eliminated the word. No need to further traumatize in order for EFT to get the job done.] *Even though I am filled with guilt, I am ok.*

TH – *All this guilt, all this guilt.*

EB – *I still see that image.*

SE – *I should have _____.*

UE – *All this guilt, all this guilt.*

UN – *I can't let it go…why didn't I _____ _____?*

Ch – *All this guilt, all this guilt.*

CB – *All this guilt — why didn't I _____?*

UA – *I should have _____.*

TH – *All this guilt.*

EB – *All this guilt.*

SE – *This guilt.*

John said he felt better, so we did a little probing to see how intense the pictures were as well as his feeling of guilt. That brief tapping brought him down to a 3.

KC – *Even though I have this remaining guilt, I choose peace.*

Even though I have this remaining guilt, I choose peace.

TH – *Remaining guilt.*

EB – *I should have _____.*

SE – *I can't forgive myself.*

UE – *All this guilt.*

UN – *Remaining guilt.*

Ch – *Remaining guilt.*

CB – *All this remaining guilt.*

I felt a shift and when I checked in with John, he reported feeling "neutral" about an event he had been carrying since 1991, or for 17 years.

He was a little stunned that this could really be the case, but he was beginning to be impressed with his EFT experience. He then shared with me that normally, after being triggered to the extent he was as we talked and worked together, his anger would have remained with him for hours.

He told me that my using the "failure" was very triggering, even though I was using his words. I asked how true that still felt and why it still seemed to feel true.

He told me that he had been involved since elementary school in some form of military association. In one way or another, the military had always been part of his identity. He was convinced that getting out of the service was a big mistake, and he simply couldn't put it behind him.

As we talked it became apparent that he was afraid he would lose memories that he treasured because the service to him was family during the times in his life when he had no family. This is something to consider when you are working with those new to EFT. They need to understand that EFT is not going to erase positive memories.

I assured him that he could put the bad behind him without losing the positive. "This isn't going to make you forget, but it will help you neutralize the emotions. Events will be things that happened but they won't continue to steal your life from you."

He said, "That's what they are doing—stealing my whole life."

Emotions were rapidly rising as he spoke about almost losing his wife because of arguments. In the moment, he was caught up in what he saw as his big mistake, leaving the service:

KC – *Even though it was all a big mistake I can't take back… I choose peace anyway. Even though there was too much going on and I didn't know how to handle it. I did the best I knew how—but I want to be happy with the way things turned out—I forgive myself. There is just too much. It is all too painful.*

TH – *How could I ever let this go?*

EB – *It is too painful. It is too big.*

SE – *But maybe if I take it one piece at a time.*

UE – *I can create peace for myself.*

UN – *Even though I feel like my past has stolen the present.*

Ch – *I choose to be in the present.*

UA – *It is too much, it is too big, I can't change it.*

TH – *Or maybe I can.*

EB – *Maybe I can embrace the present and enjoy the now.*

SE – *Letting go of all this deep sadness.*

UE – *Letting go of all this pain from the past.*

UN – *Letting go and choosing peace.*

Ch – *Letting go.*

CB – *Choosing the present.*

John's intensity was greatly reduced, but I knew we had a way to go. In an effort to reassess, I asked him

EFT for Combat Veterans

to repeat a statement about his sense of feeling lost now that he wasn't in the service any longer. He simply couldn't do it and broke into tears as he said, "I hate not being there."

Even though I hate not being there, it was my life, I feel lost without it, I choose peace. Even though I hate not being there—it was my life for so many years, I love and forgive myself. I choose peace.

TH – *It was my life, from the time I was seven—it was like my family.*

EB – *It was all I could really count on.*

SE – *I miss it.*

UE – *It was all I knew.*

UN – *From the time I was seven.*

Ch – *I miss it.*

CB – *I'm lost without it.*

UA – *I am angry and filled with despair.*

IW – *I miss it.*

OW – *I am lost without it.*

TH – *Nothing feels the same.*

The emotional ups and downs were constant, making it apparent that he was roaming through various issues and aspects. So we took a breather for a moment and I attempted to zero in on a more specific and intense aspect.

Many family circumstances made John feel that he needed to leave the service. However, 30 days later he found himself filled with regret and headed to a recruitment office for re-enlistment. They would take him back, but he would lose rank and end up taking a pay cut. He would be outranked by the very soldiers he was in charge of a month earlier. He couldn't bring himself to accept it, so he walked away. There was anger about the fact that they wouldn't check his records to see that he had already given them many years of service and was due to pick up a new rank when he left. However, as he shared this with me, additional aspects, issues, and events were making themselves known. I allowed him the opportunity to download, since in the middle of all this, he had shared with me that he was revealing things to me that he had never shared with anyone. And of course, it ended up bringing us to exactly where we needed to be, in the middle of an emotion-packed image from his daily movies.

KC – *Even though I still have this incredibly vivid image, and it still has me feeling angry and guilty because I didn't perform the way I should have, I forgive myself. Even though I can't get this image out of my mind, it is incredibly vivid—still filled with guilt and anger. I should have done it differently—I forgive myself.*

TH – *This image.*

EB – *This vivid image.*

SE – *I see it everyday.*

UE – *See it all the time.*

UN – *It really bothers me.*

Ch – *I am angry with myself.*

CB – *Disappointed in me, I failed.*

UA – *I still see that image.*

TH – *Vivid image.*

EB – *That image.*

SE – *It's with me all the time.*

UE – *I see it everyday.*

UN – *That image.*

Ch – *That vivid image.*

CB – *Still angry with myself.*

UA – *That image, I didn't do what they taught me to do.*

At this point John was doing his best to stifle a yawn. I told him to just let it happen, knowing that he was processing the many changes he was experiencing.

IW – *Vivid image.*

OW – *That vivid image.*

9G – *Didn't do what they taught me to do.*

IW – *I keep flashing back there.*

OW – *That vivid image.*

9G – *I see it everyday.*

TH – *I see it all the time.*

EB – *I see it now.*

SE – *That image.*

UE – *I am still angry with myself.*

UN – *Why didn't I do what they taught me to do.*

Ch – *I can't let this go.*

CB – *I won't let this go.*

UA – *It's my anger and you can't have it.*

TH – *It is serving me well.*

EB – *I can't let this go.*

SE – *I won't let this go.*

UE – *This vivid image.*

UN – *I can't forgive myself.*

Ch – *This image.*

CB – *This vivid image.*

UA – *All this anger with myself.*

TH – *All this anger with myself.*

John was feeling much better, so we did some testing. He reran it in his mind and then detailed the image, as best he could. There was no emotional charge and he shared with me that the image in his mind was now of his family, and his feelings were that of hope. However, in a matter of seconds, he said, "It doesn't feel bad—*for now."* When I asked about "for now," an obvious tail-ender, he told me he was sure it would pop up again later and get him fired up.

Sure, it is possible that some remnants remain to be cleared, or that new aspects including but not limited to smells or sounds might surface. But I reminded him that if that if that were the case, with a little persistent tapping he could experience the same sense of relief and hope he had today.

Concerned about his doubts and the obvious tail-ender, we went to work. Here's a sample of the language.

KC – *Even though a part of me may think this is too good to be true, and those awful feelings are bound to come back —how could I be rid of it so easily? I am willing to trust and believe in me.*

TH – *I think I like feeling better.*

EB – *I might even be able to love and forgive myself.*

SE – *This is too weird.*

UE – *How could this possibly be true after all these years?*

UN – *All these meds.*

Ch – *All those things I tried.*

CB – *Nothings made a difference.*

UA – *How could it be so simple?*

TH – *Where were you when I needed you?*

EB – *Maybe I can believe in this.*

SE – *Even though it seems unbelievable.*

UE – *Too good to be true.*

UN – *I choose to be persistent.*

Ch – *Because I know I can overcome.*

We both knew that work remained to be done, but for the first time in years he was hopeful. He asked, "Why aren't they using this stuff at the VA?"

That's a good question. I am working on it, but in the mean time we all need to be giving our all to spreading the word and getting it to as many as humanly possible, most especially to the veterans and their families.

❀ ❀ ❀

6

Exploring Underlying Issues

Every once in a while, someone tries the basic EFT formula and gets immediate, lasting results. The problem disappears in a single session and never comes back. We call these success stories "one-minute wonders," and they can and do happen, even with Post-Traumatic Stress Disorder.

But in many cases, at some point after EFT's Basic Recipe reduces or eliminates the problem or trauma, it comes back. If this happens, don't assume that EFT didn't work. EFT worked fine on the problem you treated, but now a new *aspect* has presented itself, and that aspect needs attention, too.

Introducing Aspects

Some issues have many pieces—or aspects—to them. These are actually separate issues. However, clients don't usually make this distinction unless you point it out to them. Suppose, for example, a client wants help with frightful memories regarding an automobile accident. You can apply EFT, of course, to "this accident" and you are likely to make good progress. If you don't, however, you can ask for more specifics—that is, more aspects —with a question like:

"What about the accident bothers you the most?"

Let's suppose the client says, *"Oh, the headlights, the headlights, I can still see them coming at me!"* You can then tap on *"the headlights"* or *"my fear of the headlights"* or any other verbiage that seems to fit. After the client's reaction to the headlights has been EFT'd to zero, you can then ask...

"What else about the accident bothers you?"

At this point the client may bring up other aspects such as *"The screams in the car"* or *"My anger at the other driver"* or *"My anger at the doctors,"* etc. The list can be quite long. Usually, though, it contains only one or two aspects. Tap on these other aspects until the client can no longer find anything bothersome about the accident.

As a test, ask the person to mentally "run the movie" of the accident in vivid detail. This will bring up any trailing aspects for tapping. Eventually, the client should have no emotional charge from the accident. It will just be an unfortunate event in his or her life, and that's all.

One mistake that is often made along the way, however, is to tap on "the headlights" and then ask a much-too-global, vague, or general question such as, *"How do you feel about the accident now?"* That question doesn't ask for any new aspects. It just asks for an overall feeling. If there are any other aspects (such as *"the screams in the car"*) the client will report *"no progress"* because the intensity is still there. Remember, clients don't distinguish between aspects. To them, it's all one big problem. You have to make the distinction by first recognizing that aspects exist and second, asking the right questions to bring them to the surface.

Aspects can exist with almost any emotional issue. For example,

- A war trauma can have aspects such as the sight of blood, the look in a comrade's eyes before he dies, the sound of a hand grenade, etc.

- A rape experience can have aspects such as the smell of the assailant's breath, the impact of a fist, the penetration, etc.

- A fear of public speaking can have aspects such as the sight of a microphone, the onlooking eyes of the audience, a memory of being ridiculed as a child, etc.

Another thing to recognize is that an aspect can also be an emotion. Thus, some clients report that the anger they had regarding a given event has shifted to sadness. Pick up on these clues. These different emotional aspects are taking you deeper into the problem. They are opportunities for greater healing and present you with great possibilities for mastering your craft.

Our DVD sets are loaded with live examples of aspects. I don't think you will find better examples anywhere of how to address this important subject. Pay particular attention to Dave and his fear of water in The EFT Course. This hour-long, very thorough session is a classic example of aspects and how to address them.

Aspects are important in EFT. Each aspect quali-
fies as a separate problem even when they all relate to
the same larger problem. Some problems have so many
pieces or aspects that the difficulty will not be completely
resolved until several are addressed.

Experienced EFTers often compare this procedure to
peeling an onion. You get rid of one layer only to discover another. When a problem has many layers or aspects,
neutralizing them with EFT can seem like a daunting
project. But considering how quickly those layers can
be dealt with and how beneficial the results are, the project is more exciting than intimidating. And the rewards
are priceless.

**There can be dozens or hundreds of specific
events underlying a larger issue and thus, theoreti-
cally, addressing all of them can be a tedious process.**
Fortunately, you do not have to address every specific
event to collapse the larger issue. You can usually do the
job by collapsing somewhere between five and twenty
of its table legs. This is because there is usually a com-
monality or "general theme" among those specific events.
After EFT appropriately collapses a few of the table legs,
a "Generalization Effect" occurs that serves to collapse
the rest.

The Generalization Effect is a fascinating feature of
EFT. I call it that because after you address a few related
problems with EFT, the process starts to generalize
over all of them. For example, someone who has a hundred traumatic memories of being abused usually finds
that after using EFT on only five or ten of them, they all

vanish. This is startling to some people because they have so many traumas in their life, they assume they are in for unending sessions with these techniques. Not so—at least, not usually. EFT often clears out a whole forest after cutting down just a few trees. You'll see an excellent example of this Generalization Effect in our DVD's session with Rich, the first veteran on the "Six Days at the V.A." video in the EFT Course DVD set.

Sometimes the specific event is too long and has so many pieces to it that it should be treated as a separate table top.

There is an art to identifying which issues are table tops and which are legs, but that comes with experience and practice. When in doubt, go for the smallest pieces. Your success rates will improve when you do. I've seen entire issues collapse by just addressing a small but important piece such as *"the hateful look in my father's eye."* Sometimes the entire issue can be reduced to a two-second specific event and collapsed in moments with EFT.

Discovering "Core Issues"

Core issues are the major events or problems that underlie our symptoms. When it comes to PTSD, core issues are the gold nuggets that, if we can only find and treat them with EFT, provide rapid relief.

The problem with core issues is that they're not always easy to find. We hide them from ourselves. They're painful. Our subconscious minds don't want us to go there. Our conscious minds are usually clueless—they have no idea what events or memories are lurking beneath the surface or how those events and memories might be causing pain.

This aspect of EFT never ceases to amaze me. Again and again I've worked with people while they dealt with incredibly painful memories, memories that controlled their lives and dictated where they would live, what career they would follow, what friends they would have, and everything else. Suddenly, after a few rounds of EFT tapping, they are completely transformed and no longer frightened, anxious, or afraid of old events. Instead, they're able to describe them as easily as if they were talking about the weather. As soon as old events and old memories lose their emotional charge, they lose their place of power in the subconscious mind.

The Personal Peace Procedure

In my online tutorial, I describe the *Personal Peace Procedure,* which is an easy exercise that can be worked on whenever you practice EFT. Try it now. The sooner you start, the sooner you'll experience true personal peace.

1. **Make a list.** On a blank sheet of paper, make a list of every bothersome specific event you can remember. If you don't find at least 50, you are either going at this half-heartedly or you have been living on some other planet. Many people will find hundreds.

2. **List everything.** While making your list you may find that some events don't seem to cause you any current discomfort. That's okay. List them anyway. The mere

fact that you remember them suggests a need for resolution.

3. **Give each event a title as though it is a mini-movie.** Examples: *Dad hit me in the kitchen... I stole Suzie's sandwich... I almost slipped and fell into the Grand Canyon... My third grade class ridiculed me when I gave that speech... Mom locked me in a closet for two days... Mrs. Adams told me I was stupid.*

4. **Tap for the big ones.** When the list is complete, pick out the biggest redwoods in your negative forest and apply EFT to each one of them until you either laugh about it or just can't think about it any more. Be sure to notice any aspects that may come up and consider them separate trees in your negative forest. Apply EFT to them accordingly. Be sure to keep after each event until it is resolved. After the biggest redwoods are removed, look for the next-biggest, etc.

5. **Work on at least one event movie per day**—preferably three—for three months. It takes only minutes per day. At this rate you will have resolved 90 to 270 specific events in three months. Then notice how your body feels better. Note, too, how your threshold for getting upset is much lower. Note how your relationships are better and how many of your therapy type issues just don't seem to be there any more. Revisit some of those specific events and notice how those previously intense incidents have faded into nothingness. Note any improvements in your blood pressure, pulse, and breathing ability, and other physical symptoms.

I ask you to consciously notice these things because, unless you do, the quality healing you will have undergone may be so subtle that you don't notice it. You may even dismiss it by saying, "Oh well, it was never much of a problem anyway." This happens repeatedly with EFT and thus I bring it to your awareness.

6. **If necessary, see your physician.** If you are taking prescription medications, you may feel the need to discontinue them. Please do so ONLY under the supervision of a qualified physician.

It is my hope that the Personal Peace Procedure will become a worldwide routine. A few minutes per day will make a monumental difference in school performance, relationships, health, and our quality of life. But these are meaningless words unless you put the idea into practice. As my good friend Howard Wight writes, *"If you are ultimately going to do something important that will make a real difference...do it now."*

The "Watch a Movie" and "Tell a Story" Techniques

In our search for core issues, we often use the Movie and Story Techniques. In both methods, you review a past event while tapping to reduce its emotional charge. The difference between the two is that in the Movie Technique, you watch events unfold in your mind, as though you're watching a movie, while in the Story Technique, you describe the events aloud.

The "plot" of the movie or story is usually very short. The key event lasted only a few seconds or a minute at most. However, if jumping straight to the key event is too painful, the movie or story can begin a few minutes before the key event. The event may have hurt, but its retelling doesn't have to.

Unlike psychotherapy techniques that require clients to relive unpleasant past events in excruciating detail, EFT's approach is gentle and flexible. You watch the movie or tell the story until you reach a point that feels uncomfortable. Instead of forcing yourself to push on, step back and tap until the emotional intensity fades.

When you feel comfortable again, resume the movie or story. When feelings rise up again, take a step back and tap. In this simple two-steps-forward and one-step-back process, you can revisit any trauma and neutralize its emotional impact in minutes.

Our bodies store traumas, and our mental movies are keys that unlock emotions that are stored with those traumas. Because EFT tapping reduces the emotional charge attached to past events, it transforms the traumas, memories, energy blocks, targeted body parts, and emotions that were previously locked together. With the emotional charge gone, the traumas become normal memories, the connections disappear, and the pain once associated with them vanishes as well.

The Tearless Trauma Technique

The Movie and Story Techniques are powerful and effective, but in some situations, as gentle as they are, they can be too intense, overwhelming, frightening, or unnerving.

I always remind people that in EFT, you don't have to feel worse in order to feel better. If the memory of a traumatic past event is simply too painful to think about, the Tearless Trauma Technique can help.

Since I first introduced this technique, it has been used with great success by many. However, the term "tearless" does not mean that no one has ever shed tears or experienced discomfort while using it. Indeed, some people respond with tears or other forms of distress at the mere mention of their issue. Please consider the Tearless Trauma Technique as a method for eliminating distress with a minimum of discomfort.

In most of our EFT work, we recreate specific memories and tap to neutralize their emotional charge. But in the Tearless Trauma Technique, we don't recreate anything. We just think about the event from a distance, in the most general way, while tapping.

I know that procedures that avoid or minimize emotional pain are criticized by some members of the healing community who believe that traumatic experiences must be thoroughly re-experienced before they can be completely relieved. I personally don't see why pain is at all necessary for healing to take place, although I would welcome debate on this. I feel confident saying this because I have taken care of a mountain of traumatic incidents (some of them VERY severe) and, after their healing, the clients have no interest at all in exploring insights or analyzing the "why" of their past experiences. More importantly, they are for the first time in their lives free from incapacitating emotional pain, and the results last. The pain never returns.

As soon as their energy shifts, there is a visible and obvious cognition change in the way these clients talk about once-troublesome incidents. They seem done with their issues because the resolution that is so highly valued by more intense techniques seems to take place within the EFT session with minimal pain. To me, this is so profound that it tempts me to rename the process "Peace without Pain."

The Tearless Trauma Technique works well in groups, in one-on-one sessions, and even for those working alone.

1. **Start by identifying a specific traumatic incident from your past.** Choose something that is at least three years old to minimize any complications from the dynamics of a current event. An example might be "the time my father punched me when I was 12." In contrast, "my father abused me" would be too broad because, chances are, the abuse took place over many incidents. Throughout this exercise, remind yourself to stay on your original issue because it's easy to shift to other issues as you tap.

2. **Now GUESS at what your emotional intensity would be** (on the 0–10 scale) IF you were to vividly imagine the incident. DO NOT actually imagine it (although many close their eyes and do this anyway). This GUESS is a surprisingly useful estimate, and it serves to minimize emotional pain. Write your

GUESS down. This guess represents your memory's emotional intensity.

3. **Next, develop a phrase to use for the EFT process,** such as "this father-punch emotion," and then proceed with a round of tapping.

4. **After this round of tapping, take another GUESS** as to what your emotional intensity about the subject is now and write it down.

5. **If your emotional intensity is still strong,** perform more rounds of EFT using the same phrase. In my experience, a total of three or four rounds will bring just about everyone down to GUESSES of 0 to 3.

6. **Perform another round of tapping** once you come down to acceptably low GUESSES. After this round, try to vividly imagine and actually relive the incident. Notice that this is the first time you are being asked to do this. All previous times have been relatively painless GUESSES. In my experience, just about everyone goes straight to zero and the rest are at very low numbers.

I urge everyone who works with trauma to try this. Try it on groups. Try it on individuals. Try it on war veterans, rape victims, and torture victims. Try it wherever trauma is involved, especially with those who are afraid of the intensity they usually feel when discussing or "getting into" their incident.

The energy based therapies have been very impressive in their ability to handle negative emotions. That is indelibly clear to practitioners using these procedures.

I think the above technique, properly mastered, adds a useful component to the "art of delivery."

Surrogate or Proxy Tapping

In surrogate or proxy tapping, you tap on something else—usually yourself or a photo—in place of the person you hope to help.

EFT practitioners do proxy tapping all the time when they tap in person or by phone with clients for their clients' problems. Students attending EFT workshops do it whenever they tap along with someone whose problem is being treated onstage. Anyone who taps in our instructional trainings does it, too. You will automatically do surrogate or proxy tapping whenever you work with a tapping buddy or with an EFT group.

Surrogate tapping can be used from any distance, from a few inches to thousands of miles. It can be done at any time, whenever you think of the person. You can tap on yourself for your own emotional responses at the same time, especially for emotions like worry, frustration, impatience, guilt, anger, fear, grief, or depression.

You can also do surrogate tapping to help animals, including family pets, animals in zoos or on farms, and wild animals.

There are three basic ways to proceed. You can:

- Tap as though you are the person or animal you want to help,

- Tap as though you are talking to the person or animal you want to help, or

- Tap as though you are describing the person or animal you want to help.

For example, your friend Tom hurt his back playing baseball. If you're tapping with him in person, simply tap on yourself while saying his setups along with him as both of you tap together:

Even though I hurt my back sliding into second base, I fully and completely accept myself. Even though I took a chance and it didn't pay off, I got tagged out and now my back is throbbing, I forgive and accept myself. Even though it was dumb to try stealing bases at my age, I did what I did and now I choose to release all this pain in my back…

If you're by yourself and thinking about Tom, you can tap on yourself while using the same first-person setup, above, or you can use a second-person setup, as though you are talking to Tom:

Tom, even though you hurt your back sliding into second, I fully and completely accept you. Even though you took a chance that didn't pay off, you got tagged out and now your back is throbbing, you can forgive and accept yourself. Even though you're getting a little old to be stealing bases, the game is over, and now you can release all the pain in your back…

Or you can use a third-person setup, as though you're talking about Tom:

*Even though Tom hurt his back sliding into second,
I fully and completely accept him. Even though he took
a chance that didn't pay off, he got tagged out and now
his back is throbbing, he can forgive and accept himself.
Even though he's getting a little old to be stealing bases,
the game is over, and now he can release all the pain in
his back...*

Borrowing Benefits

Did you know that tapping on behalf of others can help clear your own problems? This is one of the more unusual aspects of EFT, and it's one of the most exciting. Talk about a win-win situation. Every time you help someone else, you help yourself.

You can borrow benefits by tapping as you study this book, sending your energy to the people whose stories you're reading. You can borrow benefits by tapping as you watch our EFT seminars on DVD, or watch the news on television, or watch commercials or anything else. You can tap on behalf of characters in books, plays, movies, magazines, and online reports. You can tap on behalf of your boss, co-workers, customers, friends, neighbors, children, spouse, parents, other relatives, and people you've never met. Whenever you practice sending balanced energy their way, you'll feel better yourself. And if they're real people with real problems, your energy will make a difference in their lives as well.

You can do this tapping in person, such as while showing your brother-in-law how to relieve his sciatica, or from a distance, or by phone.

The Borrowing Benefits phenomenon is so powerful and fascinating that I conducted an entire seminar on this theme, and it's available on DVD. At the beginning of each section, I remind those watching to select a personal problem, focus on it for a moment, and then set it aside. While your conscious mind is busy tapping along with the seminar audience, your subconscious mind will include your own situation in every tapping session.

The benefits you receive, or "borrow," don't have to be related in any way to the situations you tap for. If your back is hurting, just focus for a moment on how it hurts, then give your undivided attention to the person you want to help. You can tap with a golfer to improve his swing, tap with a student to improve her grades, tap with a dieter about losing weight, or even tap for the family dog to help her indigestion—and all the while, your back will feel better.

After introducing the "Borrowing Benefits" feature of EFT, I received many enthusiastic responses. For many, it represents a big step toward speed and efficiency in the delivery of these procedures.

The process also provides an additional measure of emotional safety. As you know, EFT is normally quite gentle but a few people tune in to some pretty intense stuff and it takes awhile to bring them down. With the Borrowing Benefits feature, however, clients merely identify their issues and then tap along with someone else on an issue that is seemingly quite different. Thus a sort of detachment is injected into the process while the original issues are being addressed "in the background."

In this way it's like the Tearless Trauma Technique (see page 155).

This way of defining and approaching problems, in my experience, helps to minimize any unwanted intensity while still getting the job done. The process may or may not give complete resolution to an issue but, properly done, it is likely to at least take the edge off, and probably much more. Very efficient. Very useful. Very humane.

Borrowing Benefits can also be a superb way to conveniently get at core issues so that truly deep work can be done. An easy way to tap along with creative EFT sessions is to pick certain from our EFT training videos, which are filled with actual sessions, many of which are quite involved. You can identify your own issue and then tap along with the video while in your living room.

Here is a suggestion for Borrowing Benefits while watching television or movies from Dr. Carol Look. She writes, "I ask clients who watch a great deal of television or frequent movie theatres to tap for the characters' distress: 'Even though she feels insecure around that man…' 'Even though she won't admit the failure is her fault…' 'Even though he's afraid to confront the situation…' The clients do not have to identify their own issues first, just tap for the distress that their own system can't help but tune into as a result of witnessing someone else's discomfort on the big screen."

This is a clever way of helping the subconscious mind neutralize some of the emotional charge connected to past events, making it easier to recognize, deal with, or simply release old problems. Tapping on behalf of fictional characters or real people you've never met brings you as many benefits as tapping on behalf of your best friend. Isn't that fascinating?

Touch and Breathe (TAB) Method

Not everyone enjoys or can do the vigorous, lively tapping that most EFTers employ, and in some situations—such as during a business meeting or when dining in public—tapping just doesn't feel comfortable for most people.

An effective alternative is the Touch and Breathe, or TAB, method developed by John Diepold, PhD. Instead of tapping on each acupoint, simply hold it with a fingertip while breathing in and breathing out. Start by holding your Sore Spot or Karate Chop point, or hold your hands together with Karate Chop points touching, while saying your Setup Phrase out loud or to yourself. Then touch and hold each of the EFT acupoints while taking a full breath in and out.

The Sequence takes longer this way, but it can be more comfortable and relaxing, and it works. Some EFTers gently massage the acupoints, which is something many of us do instinctively while thinking or concentrating. We rub or press the upper lip, hold the Under Arm points while hugging ourselves, stroke the collarbone, or scratch the head.

To stimulate the hand points, hold each finger between the thumb and forefinger of the "tapping" hand while breathing in and breathing out, or place your fingertips together (index fingers touching, thumbs touching, etc.) and breathe. To activate the wrist points, simply circle your wrist with the opposite hand and hold it while breathing, or cross your wrists so they touch each other. To access the ankle points, reach down and touch the ankles while breathing, or simply cross your ankles so that they touch each other.

7

Improving
EFT's Effectiveness

Those who are new to EFT often ask when and how frequently they should practice tapping. The answer is: As often as you like—or, better yet, as often as possible. EFT is very flexible and forgiving. The more often you practice, the sooner EFT becomes a familiar tool that you can use without effort. The more you use it, the better it works. The more you use it, the more likely you are to remember to use it when you really need it.

I usually recommend that you start by tapping *as soon as you wake up in the morning, before every meal, and before falling asleep at night.*

That's five times a day right there. Tap whenever you use the bathroom or take a shower and you'll add a few more. Some EFTers tap whenever they come to a stop sign or red light. Quite a few tap while they walk. You don't have to do the entire Basic Recipe—just a few quick taps as time permits will help keep your energy balanced —and as soon as you have enough time, follow up with the complete sequence. Many EFTers tap before, during, or after they pray or meditate. EFT tapping can improve any project or activity.

When you're in a hurry, try tapping on a single point, such as the Karate Chop point, while you focus on your pain or problem. In one workshop I completely forgot to include the EFT tapping points. All we did was tap on the Karate Chop point while reciting a Setup, with excellent results.

In addition, if you get in the habit of tapping on the EFT acupoints without reciting a Setup or focusing your thoughts on anything specific, that alone will help keep your energy balanced and help you live a happier life.

Try tapping to music. This is a popular activity in some EFT workshops—it keeps the group focused and energetic, and it's an easy way to avoid an energy slump in the afternoon. Teaching children to tap to music is a great way to introduce them to EFT. Tap at whatever rhythm feels right. Experiment with classical music, rock, ballads, rap, opera, marches, movie soundtracks, or whatever you most enjoy.

Tap while you read your email or work at the computer. Tap while you watch TV. Tap while you talk on the phone. Tap while you study—that's an easy way to improve your reading comprehension and recall. Tap right now as you read this page.

If you tap while you describe things that you've seen or experienced, your recollections are more likely to be accurate. In fact, EFT would probably significantly improve the accuracy of eye-witness testimony. In EFT, we use the "Tell a Story," "Watch a Movie," and Tearless Trauma Techniques (see pages 152–157) to help people describe difficult events without feeling emotionally overwhelmed. With their emotions under control, they are able to think, remember, and process information more efficiently. Several EFT practitioners have reported on tapping's incredible calming effect when applied immediately after an accident, tragedy, or disaster.

Here's a great tip from EFT practitioner Rick Wilkes, which appeared in our online newsletter. I think it has special application for those experiencing PTSD because it deals with underlying issues easily and automatically, without conscious effort. Many have found that their way of looking at a situation changes as a result of following Rick's simple instructions.

The Tap-While-You-Gripe Technique
by Rick Wilkes

Have you ever called a friend just to gripe about everything that's gone wrong in your day? The truth is that when things go wrong, we need to feel that we're not alone. So we turn to trusted friends and family to let off steam and be comforted. It's a natural part of being human. Most of us have been expressing our pain this way since we were very young children.

What I call "griping" is just a way to retell a story with emotional intensity. And there is scientific proof that this can help us. Recent brain studies show that there's an *opportunity* when we relive an experience to have the stored emotions of that experience heal... or become even more intense. As we recall the story and feel the emotions in our body, our brain is making a decision—one that can go either way!

That is why I suggest that you always tap while you gripe. Tap while you complain. Tap every time you tell a story that has negative emotional intensity. Pretty soon, you'll probably notice you have a lot less in your life to gripe about!

Here's how you can get started:

You've had a bad day. You want to feel that there's someone out there that understands you, that cares about you, that takes your side. So you pick up the phone, and you call your best friend. Start tapping… and tap continuously while you talk to her!

(Karate Chop) – *Ring… Ring… Hello?*

(Top of Head) – *Oh I'm so glad I reached you.*

(Inside Eyebrow) – *I have had such a terrible day!*

(Side of Eye) – *I really need someone to talk to.*

(Under Eye) – *Do you have a few minutes?*

(Under Nose) – *First off, this *e3^+$ boss of mine…*

(then Chin, Collarbone, Under Arm, Karate Chop, and back to Top of Head, etc.)

The order of the points doesn't matter. The number of taps at each point doesn't matter. You can tap one point that feels good the whole call if you want.

You can use the finger points. Just tap continuously while you talk. Don't stop!

Why would we do this? We talk to others to feel better, don't we? But there are two approaches to griping and complaining. The first is, alas, the more common. It is to gather people to our side in the upcoming war. We tell a story to make us "right" and the other party "wrong." With this plan, we must *build* intensity in ourselves and in others while we plan revenge (or a lawsuit, divorce, or other dramatic action designed so we WIN and the other LOSES).

The other approach is to want to *heal* from an emotional pain, and we're mature enough to know that intensifying the fear by making us the "Victims" and others into the "Powerful Forces of True Evil" just creates war inside us, not peace.

We can make our healing far more likely if we just tap the acupoints while we express our hurt and our anger and our sadness and our feelings of being out of control. We use what has been human nature since cave folks sat around the fire—the need to tell our story to tribe members to gain their supportive energy—and we use that supportive energy in a new way that is far more likely to result in a sense of peace for all of us.

What I find is that tapping while I gripe and complain shifts my entire perspective. As the noise of the emotional disruption settles down, I am far more likely to hear my intuition guide me to steps that resolve the situation in the best possible way.

Try it for yourself. Tap the acupoints while you are on the phone. No one needs to know that you are tapping. And just notice whether you see a change that helps you feel both more peaceful and more empowered. I am confident you will.

In fact, you may find this so effective that you pick up your phone and tap while you gripe without even calling your friend. Once you get it all out of your system, then you dial…and perhaps have a very different kind of conversation.

❊ ❊ ❊

Can You Do EFT Incorrectly?

This is an interesting question. EFT is so forgiving and versatile that finding ways in which it doesn't work can be a challenge. In fact, many EFTers respond that the only way to do it wrong is to not use it.

You can do an incomplete EFT treatment (which will make more sense as we explore advanced concepts), but if you combine focused thought and intention with tapping, your efforts will probably work no matter what Setup or Tapping Sequence you use.

For example, you can omit the words "Even though" and simply state the problem:

> *My back hurts.*
>
> *I can't sleep through the night.*
>
> *I'm upset.*

And you don't have to tap on the EFT acupoints in any specific order. I recommend the Sequence described in the Basic Recipe because it's easy to remember, but you can tap the points in any order, on either side or on both sides, upside down or right side up, and you'll still get great results.

And the list goes on. I believe that if your intention is to treat a specific issue and you combine that intention with any type of acupoint stimulation, you can expect good results.

When I created EFT, I streamlined more complicated meridian therapies that involved separate algorithms or tapping patterns for different conditions or symptoms. Each had its own tapping pattern. An algorithm for chronic pain, for example, started at the Inside Eyebrow point and went to Side of Eye, Under Eye, Under Nose, Collarbone, Under Arm, Little Finger, Collarbone, Index Finger, and Collarbone, then ended with 50 taps on the Gamut point. An algorithm for anger, bitterness, and resentment moved from Inside Eyebrow to Little Finger to Collarbone. An algorithm for emotional trauma went from the Inside Eyebrow to Side of Eye, Under Eye, Under Arm, Collarbone, Thumb, Under Arm, Collarbone, Little Finger, Collarbone, and Index Finger.

I realized that these algorithms, which are difficult to remember, especially in emergencies, could be replaced with a single tapping pattern. By the time you complete three or more rounds of tapping on the EFT acupoints, you've tapped on all of the points in a variety of combinations. The beauty of meridian therapies is that when you stimulate points that you don't need, you don't hurt yourself or cause complications—and when you tap on points that you do need, the process works.

At first I replaced algorithms with a single tapping sequence and created EFT's Basic Recipe. Then I put the 9 Gamut treatment on the shelf, for use only when I'm stuck. I did the same with the finger points. These tools are worth learning because they can be very helpful, but if you get good results without them, why use them? Save them for when you need them.

I now encourage people to find their own "personal" EFT acupoint and try it first. Most of us, if we pay attention, realize that we're drawn to a certain point, or we notice that every time our energy shifts, it's when we're tapping on the same point. For some it's the Under Eye; for many, it's the Under Arm or Karate Chop point. For me, it's the Collarbone point. If you set out to relieve your back pain and you tap on a single acupoint and the pain goes away, you're done. What could be simpler?

Conditions That Interfere

Now let's consider some of the conditions that can interfere with your ability to neutralize traumatic memories and reduce or eliminate the symptoms of PTSD, all of which can be addressed with EFT.

Psychological Reversal

The first obstacle that can interfere is your energy flow. If your energy is flowing in the right direction, without obstacles or blockages, you're on your way. If your energy is blocked or reversed, the problem we call *psychological reversal* or *polarity reversal* interferes.

As described in the Basic Recipe, tapping on the Karate Chop point or massaging the Sore Spot corrects this problem and gets the energy flowing as it should. It's possible to test for psychological reversal with kinesiology (muscle testing), but we save time by assuming that we might be psychologically reversed—it's a state that we all move in and out of several times a day—and simply correct the reversal before we start tapping. Thus, your Setup performs two vital functions: it focuses your mind on the problem you want to address, and it corrects psychological reversal if it happens to be in effect.

Self-talk and the "Writings on Your Walls"

The second potential stumbling block is your subconscious mind and its programming, which is reflected by your *self-talk*, the thoughts and statements that rattle around in your head at all hours of the day and night that have anything to do with you.

I call your self-talk's programming the *writings on your walls*. This writing contains all of the "rules" you grew up with or absorbed through life experiences—statements you heard as a child, which reflect your family or cultural conditioning, or ideas or attitudes, especially about yourself, that you've absorbed throughout your life.

> *Life is dangerous.*
>
> *You can't be too careful. Everyone has a hidden agenda.*
>
> *It's all my fault.*
>
> *I don't deserve to be happy.*

It's important to never show weakness.

I'm just not good in relationships.

Tail-enders

Closely related to the writings on our walls are the *tail-enders* they inspire. Tail-enders are the "yes, but" statements that pop up when we try to set new goals or write new affirmations.

The most obvious tail-enders are the words we hear in our minds when we try out a new idea. These words often have a sarcastic ring to them: *Yeah, right. When pigs fly. I'll believe that when I see it. You must be kidding. Forget it. No way. Impossible.*

They are the nemesis of affirmations. A standard piece of advice in metaphysical circles is to turn negative self-talk around by stating the opposite. For example, if you hear yourself saying, "This is going to be a terrible day," try switching that to, "This is a wonderful day." If your conscious and subconscious minds accept the affirmation, it probably will be a wonderful day—but what if they don't? That's when tail-enders create mischief.

Tail-enders can show up at the end of a "Choices" statement, where you describe your goal, such as in this example:

Even though I feel angry all the time, I choose to stay calm and relaxed, no matter who is trying to get me upset...

...but I know that's never going to happen.

...but I've always been this way and it's too hard to change.

...but I can't let people take advantage of me.

...but there are some things I just can't let go of.

...but it's too dangerous to let my guard down.

Whenever you notice a tail-ender, see it for what it is, an important clue that is pointing to core issues. Where did that idea come from? Can you hear someone's voice in your head, like the voice of your mother, father, teacher, neighbor, or friend? What events from long ago come to mind? Every memory or event can be put to good use as a Setup that combines tail-enders with the writings on your walls.

When demonstrating EFT in workshops or when working with clients, EFT practitioners often create "fill in the blank" statements and wait for the person to complete the sentence. For example,

When I think about how important it is not to let people take advantage of me, I remember _____.

When I relax and let my mind drift back to my childhood, I can hear my dad's voice saying, "_____ _____."

Even though I can never forgive _____ for _____...

As soon as a specific memory appears, you can turn it into a Setup:

Even though my dad always said I was an out-of-control hothead, I fully and completely accept myself...

Even though I got in a fight with Eddie Jackson in high school, and my folks said they were giving up on me...

Continue revising the Setup so that it focuses on the person's emotions:

Even though my dad did nothing but criticize and scowl at me, and it really hurt because I could never get his approval no matter how hard I tried, and it made me really mad, in fact it still does, and just the sight of him standing there would turn my stomach, I would like to let go of that unhappy time...

Saying Goodbye to the Past

Another way to release core issues that contribute to self-sabotage is to tap while saying:

Even though _____ happened, it doesn't have to bother me any more. Even though _____ happened and I can't change the past, I can change my emotional connection to the past. Even though _____ happened, it doesn't have to affect me any more, I can relax about it and let it go, I can function in the present moment.

As soon as you start building on the Basic Recipe by experimenting, trying new approaches, and exploring new ways of presenting and using EFT, you will achieve faster and more remarkable results.

How to Tell Whether EFT Is Working

Did your tapping make a difference? When the problem is pain, the test is simple—either the pain goes away or it doesn't. If it does, it's probably because EFT successfully removed energy blocks while neutralizing emotional issues that were the pain's underlying cause. But pain relief isn't the only indication of EFT's effectiveness. Here are some common signs of EFT at work in any tapping session.

- **The person sighs.** This often happens after a round of tapping and it reflects an energy shift away from stress toward relaxation.

- **The person yawns.** The yawn might or might not be accompanied by fatigue. Some people have fallen asleep in the middle of their EFT sessions, but even well-rested people yawn during and after tapping.

- **The person's breathing changes.** Most of us breathe shallowly, especially when we're under stress. Longer, slower, deeper breaths are almost always a signal that EFT is working. The more balanced your energy, the smoother and more relaxed your breathing.

- **The person's voice changes.** During an EFT session it's not uncommon for someone's voice to crack, for stress or tension to make the voice actually squeak, or for the person to have trouble talking. Then, after EFT brings the person's energy into balance, his or her voice sounds deeper, rounder, fuller, more confident, stronger, and more vibrant. Speech patterns change, too, going from stumbling and inarticulate to clear, coherent, fluid, and eloquent.

- **The person's posture and body language change.** People who are depressed, anxious, frightened, or in pain sit, stand, and walk very differently from the way they do when they're comfortable, confident, relaxed, happy, and healthy. In successful EFT sessions, postural changes are often obvious. Instead of sitting hunched, with the head down and a curved spine, most people straighten up, lift their heads, and look at the world around them.

- **The person cries.** The Tearless Trauma Technique (see page 155) is at the heart of EFT, and it really is possible to work through serious problems without weeping. But in many cases people do cry. Tears are often a sign of release or relief. Even if the tears are a symptom of discomfort, in which case the Tearless Trauma Technique is used to reduce the discomfort level, the emotional change indicates that EFT is working.

- **Sinuses drain.** Congested sinuses that suddenly to drain reflect an energy shift.

- **Facial muscles relax.** Actually, muscles all over the body soften, but changes in facial expression, such as from tense and stressed to relaxed and comfortable, are obvious clues. EFT can make such a difference in facial expression that some practitioners call it an instant face-lift. A few rounds of effective tapping can help you look years younger as well as happier.

- **Blood pressure and pulse change.** Often people begin an EFT session with an elevated pulse rate or high blood pressure. In those cases, successful EFT tapping—even if it's for something unrelated to physical symptom—brings both pulse and blood pressure back to normal.

- **The person feels hot or cold.** A temperature change, such as feeling suddenly hot or cold, is another indication that EFT is working. A small or large area of back pain may feel intensely warm or hot, and the pain may pulse or vibrate. Someone who feels suddenly hot may blush or turn red. Another person might break out in a cold sweat and suddenly feel chilled. All of these physiological changes indicate that EFT is working.

- **The person feels vibrating energy.** Do enough tapping and your fingers will begin to tingle. When that happens, move your open hands toward each other, moving them closer, further apart, and closer again. If you sense a vibrating energy field or a feeling of resistance that grows stronger as your hands move closer, something is happening energetically.

- **A cognitive shift occurs.** One minute you're angry and the next you're laughing. One minute the person you're mad at can't do anything right and the next you're making excuses for him. One minute you're convinced that there is only one way, one "right" and "true" way, to look at the situation and the next you realize there are many. As soon as you stop replaying a situation in the same old way and notice something new or different, and as soon as "the principle of the thing" no longer matters the way it did, it's obvious that EFT has done its job.

- **The pain moves.** In EFT sessions that involve physical pain, this happens so often that we use the phrase "chasing the pain" to describe the appropriate EFT response. The pain might move a short distance, such as an inch or two, but it's often a longer distance, such as from the left eye to the right side of the forehead or from the right shoulder blade to the center of the spine. In some cases pain jumps all over the body.

- **The pain gets worse.** Ironically, this can be a sign that EFT is working. It often indicates that buried emotional issues are getting close to the surface. By continuing to tap and by approaching the pain and its aspects from a different perspective, your results will probably improve. It's very unusual for pain to get worse and stay worse when you're using EFT, especially when you incorporate the many shortcuts and advanced techniques explained in this book.

- **The person is suddenly open to new options.** This is an excellent sign because it shows that the person is no longer stuck in his or her old way of thinking and feeling. Balanced energy leads to clear thinking.

The overall test is whether *any* kind of change is taking place. The more things change, the more energy is moving and the more EFT is working. Even if you haven't yet achieved the results you hope for, all this moving energy is a very good sign. It's only when nothing happens—the pain stays exactly where it was, the person's attitude doesn't shift at all, and the whole situation stays stuck—that we are tempted to conclude that EFT was not effective.

Even when that happens, it's worth trying again. So much depends on the art of delivery, the search for core issues, and the examination of different aspects that a sudden breakthrough can turn an unresponsive situation into an EFT success story. I've seen this so many times that I never conclude that EFT "didn't work." Rather, I adopt the belief that EFT always works but that sometimes we have to keep searching for the problem's true emotional cause.

The next chapter will help you develop the EFT skills that bring outstanding results for yourself and everyone you'd like to help, including friends, relatives, total strangers, and even family pets. In fact, people have reported using EFT to improve the health of their house plants and the performance of their cars, computers, and household appliances.

I shouldn't be surprised. After all, I told them to try it on everything! And you can, too.

8

Choices, Solutions and Tapping Tips

Dr. Patricia Carrington's "Choices" Method

Patricia Carrington, Ph.D., Associate Clinical Professor at the UMDNJ-Robert Wood Johnson Medical School in New Jersey, was one of the first clinical psychologists to incorporate EFT into her professional practice. She not only became a leading practitioner of Emotional Freedom Techniques, she made an important contribution to its Setup.

Basic or mechanical EFT focuses entirely on problems. It starts with statements like, "Even though I have this pain in my back..." or, "Even though my shoulder is in agony..." and ends with the phrase, "I deeply and completely accept myself." The treatment then proceeds with the repetition of a "problem" reminder phrase such as the phrase, "This pain."

There's no doubt that by using this type of Setup, you can tap a problem out. But Dr. Carrington took a different approach and showed that you can also tap a solution in.

She did this by adding "I choose" to the last portion of the Setup, making it possible for the person to define or describe a specific desired outcome by inserting an affirmation or positive statement after the words "I choose."

As she explains:

When I was using EFT with my own clients in psychotherapy, I soon discovered that I could get even better results if I allowed them to insert their own positive affirmations into the EFT statement. This way the Setup became perfectly suited to the problems they were addressing.

For example, if a person's hand was throbbing, I would suggest an EFT statement such as, "Even though my hand is throbbing, I choose to have my hand be comfortable and pain free." This immediately makes perfect sense to the injured person; it expresses precisely what they want to bring about—the cessation of pain and the healing of their hand.

It was through experimenting with my own clients that the EFT Choices Method was born. In it, the person applying the method identifies the outcome that they would truly like to have for the problem at hand, and then puts this desired outcome into a phrase which they use at the end of the Setup. Instead of "I deeply and completely accept myself," this phrase commences with the words "I choose."

It's important to note that "I choose" is not used in the format of a traditional affirmation. The latter is a statement that is intentionally contrary to fact, as, for example when a person living in a dingy basement apartment says, "I live in a beautiful sunny home." This statement is intentionally contrary to fact. According to the rules of traditional affirmations it will result in subconscious programming that attracts the "beautiful sunny" home of the person's dreams. All too often, however, traditional affirmations result in doubt and skepticism on the part of those who repeat them, particularly if the affirmation is in too sharp a contrast to their current state of affairs.

When people tell themselves that they live in a beautiful sunny home when in fact that is obviously not true, the traditional affirmation is apt to create what EFT refers to as a "Tail-ender." A little doubting self-statement in the back of our minds says, "Oh yeah? I know that's absurd!" or "I'll NEVER have that! " or "I feel like a fool for saying this."

Such self-doubts are stilled, however, when you place the words "I choose" at the beginning of your affirmation statement. For example, if the person described above were to say, "Even though I live in a dingy basement apartment, I choose to live in a lovely sunny home," the statement would be immediately believable because anyone has the right to make a "choice" and this doesn't contradict the situation they are in.

This method of injecting "Choices" into EFT soon developed into a definite protocol which I found to be extremely effective, not only for my own clients and workshop participants, but for many others as well. I then formalized the Choices Method and began training other people to use it. It was almost immediately greeted with enthusiasm in the EFT community, and today many thousands of people are using EFT Choices statements. In particular, psychotherapists, counselors, and personal performance coaches are using the Choices Method because it so precisely targets their clients' problems.

❋ ❋ ❋

Dr. Carrington's six rules for phrasing Choices statements are sensible and effective:

1. Be specific.
2. Create *pulling* Choices.
3. Go for the best possible outcome
4. State your Choices in the positive.
5. Make Choices that apply to you.
6. Make Choices that are easy to pronounce.

"Pulling Choices" use words that draw you in and make you feel involved. They are the opposite of dull and boring statements. Dr. Carrington begins with the example, "I choose to express myself in a way that gets my points across to Susan," which is a perfectly accurate statement as far as it goes. But, she says, an even more appealing version might be, "I choose to find a *creative way* to get my points across to Susan." As she explains, the word *creative* gives the statement some excitement and suspense. You wonder what would be a creative way to get your points across. As she says, "Curiosity is a powerful motivator." *Surprise* is another word that can draw us in, so another effective statement could be, "I choose to *surprise myself* by finding easy and enjoyable ways to get my points across to Susan." *Easy* and *enjoyable* are pulling words, too, and they help make this a compelling statement.

Here's an example of a Setup that falls short of the six recommendations:

> *Even though my back hurts, I choose to have it not hurt.*

Following Dr. Carrington's suggestions, we can add specific details about the pain, insert some interesting or compelling ideas, describe what we'd rather have, replace negative words (no, not, can't, won't, etc.) with positive words, and create a personally rewarding Choices Phrase. For example:

> *Even though I have this sharp, red, throbbing, angry, hard, pyramid-shaped pain stabbing the small of my back just to the left of my spine, I choose to be delighted by how easy it is to enjoy a relaxed, pain-free game of golf tomorrow, with full range of motion, perfect coordination, and my best score yet.*

While tapping on the EFT acupoints, try alternating between "problem" and "solution" reminder phrases.

For example, in the first round of tapping, use "problem" reminders:

> Top of Head: *stabbing pain*
>
> Inside Eyebrow: *so frustrating*

Side of Eye: *terrible pain*

Under Eye: *can't move*

and so on, through all the tapping points

Or use the same complete "problem" sentence on all of the acupoints, such as:

Top of Head: *I'm upset because my back is in agony.*

Inside Eyebrow: *I'm upset because my back is in agony.*

Side of Eye: *I'm upset because my back is in agony.*

and so on, through all the tapping points.

Then, in the second round of tapping, use only positive "solution" phrases, such as:

Top of Head: *better already*

Inside Eyebrow: *pain-free*

Side of Eye: *complete range of motion*

Under Eye: *everything's easy*

and so on, through all the tapping points

Or use the same complete "solution" sentence on all of the acupoints, such as:

Top of Head: *I choose to feel completely well in every way.*

Inside Eyebrow: *I choose to feel completely well in every way.*

Side of Eye: *I choose to feel completely well in every way*

and so on, through all the tapping points.

In the third and final round of tapping, alternate between "problem" and "solution" phrases, such as:

Top of Head: *stabbing pain*

Inside Eyebrow: *I feel wonderful*

Side of Eye: *sharp spasms*

Under Eye: *full range of motion*

Under Nose: *so frustrating*

and so on, through all the tapping points, always ending on a "solution" phrase.

Or alternate between the two complete sentences used above:

Top of Head: *I'm upset because my back is in agony.*

Inside Eyebrow: *I choose to feel completely well in every way.*

Side of Eye: *I'm upset because my back is in agony.*

Under Eye: *I choose to feel completely well in every way.*

and so on, through all the tapping points.

To be sure your final phrase is positive (you should always end on a positive note), finish by tapping on the Inside Eyebrow point while saying a positive re minder phrase.

Some practitioners start with problem reminder phrases in the first round of tapping, alternate between problem and solution reminder phrases in the second, and devote the third round entirely to solution statements.

Some begin with the basic EFT Setup ("Even though _____, I fully and completely accept myself," or something similar) for their first two Setups and switch to Choices phrasing for the third setup.

Some use only one Setup and incorporate everything in it before they start tapping the acupoints. Like EFT itself, the Choices Method is flexible, and there is no single "right" way to use it.

The Choices Method is brilliant because it helps people figure out not only what they don't want but what they do want, it installs affirmations and positive statements, and it helps speed results. Patricia Carrington is truly an EFT pioneer, and I applaud her discoveries.

❊ ❊ ❊

Dr. Carol Look offers ten innovative tapping tips that can help experts and novices alike improve their results. All of these can help take your EFT skills to the next level.

Top Ten Tapping Tips
by Dr. Carol Look

I have compiled a list of my favorite tapping tips that have had a dramatic influence on my work and results with clients. Use any that work for you, but I highly recommend trying them all before you dismiss them, especially the ultra simple ones.

1. Opposite Hand Tapping:

When tapping on yourself, use your non-dominant hand for a full day, then switch to your dominant hand on the following day, and back again the next day. You could also alternate hands from round to round of EFT. In my opinion, alternating in this way helps because it allows you to more fully integrate the emotional material that you are working on. Of course, we usually favor one side, tending to be right-handed or left-handed, so making use of the "other" hand while tapping through emotional conflicts helps to more fully neutralize the issues. For those who do telephone sessions as either client or practitioner, switch the phone from side to side regularly as well, so alternating ears are "hearing."

Here is another variation...*Cross Over Tapping:* Cross your hands over each other when you tap—so your right hand is tapping on your left side of your face and body, and your left hand is tapping on the right...at the same time. Also, consider tapping while in different positions. Aren't you always sitting down while tapping? Try standing up when using EFT, try lying down, and tap while you are rolled over on your side. Notice if any new material surfaces. Our bodies are brilliant, and they have stored so much information for us.

2. Argument Tapping

I love using this process with clients in a group setting because most people find it surprising and amusing and seem to get something of value out of it. When you are tapping, voice both sides of an argument with another person around an issue of self-esteem or conflict about yourself. For instance, let's say your mother or father said you "wouldn't amount to anything" or that "people like you can't get wealthy" or that "people like you are never satisfied," etc. Take both sides and argue the points while you tap, alternating the sides with each consecutive point. For instance, start with the karate chop point, and say, *Even though he said I was no good and wouldn't amount to anything, I choose to accept myself now anyway...* Then move to the regular sequence of points and tap as if you are arguing with another person as follows:

Eyebrow: *You won't amount to anything...*

Side of Eye: *Yes, I will...*

Under Eye: *No you won't...*

Under Nose: *Yes I wil...*

Chin: *Don't be ridiculous...*

Collarbone: *I'm smart enough...*

Under Arm: *Who are you kidding?*

Top of Head: *I know I can do it...*

Be sure to follow how the argument is "looping" in your memory, and vigorously argue both sides. This will help chop down a lot of "trees in your forest."

Proceed with other similar arguments. The Argument Tapping technique is wonderful for the brain, for the emotional release, and I expect that the absurdity of it all will surface for many of you and feel quite relieving.

This is also useful for getting the tail-enders into your tapping. The next variation of Argument Tapping is to argue with *yourself* while tapping. When you are tapping and saying something positive, for instance, *I know I have what it takes to be successful*...you might "hear" a tail-ender that says *"No I don't!"* Use whatever tail-enders that come up for you in your current round of EFT. So again, you are arguing, but this time with yourself. It would sound like this:

Eyebrow: *I have what it takes to be successful...*

Side of Eye: *No I don't...*

Under Eye: *I am smart enough to figure this out...*

Under Nose: *No I'm not!*

Chin: *Yes I am!*

Collarbone: *No I'm not...*

Under Arm: *I accept my feelings...*

Top of Head: *I appreciate who I am...*

3. Refusal Tapping

When you are using EFT, do one full round of Refusal Tapping to get over the issue you have selected. We have all been told what to do, controlled on a regular basis, influenced by others and manipulated all our lives, and when trying to change, it is very natural to experience an enormous amount of emotional resistance. Part of us believes the change is threatening to our survival. Try giving this part of you a voice for a change, and feel the relief of saying "No!" Don't be surprised when this technique speeds up the change you were intending. Refusal Tapping is very helpful with chronic illnesses. Your round from the eyebrow point to the top of the head would proceed as follows:

Eyebrow: *I refuse to give this up...*

Side of Eye: *Don't even try to make me...*

Under Eye: *I am so happy I don't have to get rid of this...*

Under Nose: *I refuse to change...*

Chin: *You can't make me...*

Collarbone: *Ha ha, I'm keeping this problem...*

Under the Arm: *You can't make me get over this...*

Top of the Head: ***I refuse to let go of this issue.***

4. Look in the Mirror

While tapping several rounds in a row, look into the mirror. This will help you in several areas. This extra boost encourages you to absorb the positive affirmation of the setup more fully *(I deeply and completely love and accept myself)*.

It helps when you need to use visualization instead of regular tapping if you are in a public place and don't feel free to tap on your face and body. You will now have a picture and corresponding memory of what you look like when you tap.

This technique allows you to see subtle changes that occur in muscle tone, color, and energy in your face and body as you tap. Definitely make use of these clues.

Look into a mirror as you tap for your deepest emotional conflicts. This works especially well for chronic low self-esteem issues.

Sometimes my clients who are calling for a phone session from their office look at their reflection in their computer screen to enhance the emotional release during the session.

In the same way that affirmations will automatically bring up a "tail-ender," looking in the mirror when you say "I deeply and completely accept myself" will trigger discomfort that is then exposed and addressed during the treatment.

5. Singing Affirmations (while you tap)

You may either sing the entire round from negative to positive, or just use singing on the second round when you are "installing" the positive statements. As usual, I do the first round focusing on the "problem" and often switch during a second round (before doing setups again) to more positive statements (such as Pat Carrington's "Choices"), goals, and intentions. So during this second round, sing your affirmations instead of speaking them. This helps activate the right brain (which is why we use humming in the 9-gamut procedure) and any time we are doing something to promote balance between our two hemispheres of the brain, we are moving towards emotional and physical health.

6. Thank-you Tapping

Do at least three rounds in a row while tapping on your "Thank You List." For example:

Eyebrow: *Thank you God (Spirit, Universe, Higher Power, Source, Universal Intelligence) for such an abundance of loving friends in my life.*

Side of Eye: *Thank you God for bringing me the perfect clients for my business.*

Under the Eye: *Thank you God for resolving that disagreement so quickly.*

Under the Nose: *Thank you God for bringing that wonderful miracle through me to my client who was in pain.*

Chin: *Thank you God for my vibrant health and energy.*

Collarbone: *Thank you God for all the blessings I have in my life today.*

Under Arm: *Thank you God for bringing me such peace in my life.*

Top of the Head: *Thank you God for continued guidance and clarity on my path.*

7. Guest Tapping

When you are tapping at home alone, wouldn't you like some extra help? Choose your favorite EFT practitioner, someone you want to give a test run, or Gary Craig, and pretend he or she is tapping for and with you. Picture it, feel it, hear the person's voice (you might have this in your head from a class or some of the videos). This will help those of you who don't think you're good enough at tapping (even though you are…) and it opens up your treatment options tremendously. Allow your intuition to choose someone. And don't be surprised when the "guest tapper" comes up with profoundly brilliant ideas!

8. Photo Tapping

Take out old family photos and identify feelings, themes, incidents and thoughts that were going on when the pictures were taken. You might even take out your high school year book (since High School seems to be so fraught with conflicted feelings for many people…) and tap a few rounds while you are looking at yourself. You may be shocked at how effective this is for bringing up emotions you thought had been "handled." Here are some options:

Look at yourself in the selected photo objectively, and use words as if you are treating someone else… *Even though he was feeling so vulnerable back then, he has a good heart and meant well… Even though he was so scared back then, he's a great person and has really matured.*

Use the first person singular… *Even though I was miserable during this time because of that incident, I deeply and completely love and accept myself… Even though I was feeling so sad because of the rejection… Even though I was confused… Even though I didn't realize I was such a geek.*

198 EFT for PTSD

Do the same for family members when you see them in the photos: *Even though he was angry and said that hurtful thing to me...I deeply and completely love and accept myself... Even though he was drunk in that photo and I remember the fight we had, I choose to release the pain of it now and accept both of us.*

9. Past Tense Tapping

After completing two or three rounds on whatever issue you have chosen, do a final round in the past tense, feeling what it would feel like if you had completely gotten over the problem (even if you haven't yet). Communicating to yourself this way is very effective. Really *feel* the relief now that it is over!! This is critical.

Eyebrow: *I am so grateful I got over this problem...*

Side of Eye: *I'm so relieved this is over...*

Under Eye: *I am so happy I am free of this conflict...*

Under Nose: *It's about time I got over that!*

Chin: *Finally, it is in my past where it belongs...*

Collarbone: *At last, relief and peace on this issue...*

Under Arm: *I so appreciate all the progress I have made...*

Top of Head: *Finally, I feel peace from that problem.*

10. "You" Tapping

While tapping on one of your own issues, use the "second person singular" over and over. For example, Setups at the karate chop point would be: *Even though you made a mistake, you were trying to do it right and are allowed not to be perfect... Even though you didn't mean to hurt her, consider accepting all of you and your feelings... Even though you don't want to forgive yourself, try accepting your feelings anyway.* Then tap the points using "you" as the subject:

> Eyebrow: *You made a mistake...*
>
> Side of Eye: *So what?*
>
> Under Eye: *You meant well...*
>
> Under the Nose: *You are human...*
>
> Chin: *You don't need to be perfect...*
>
> Collarbone: *You are lovable anyway...*
>
> Under Arm: *You are such a good person...*

Top of head: *You are totally lovable and worthy anyway.*

11. Kiss and Tap

Here's a bonus tapping tip. Kiss someone you love on all the face points and say I love you. Great for kids! Great for lovers! Also, kiss yourself on the finger points of both hands, the karate chop point on both sides, the gamut spot, and any other spots you can reach. Do this very tenderly.

❊ ❊ ❊

When EFT Doesn't Work

EFT can work in the most extreme conditions, when many factors could be expected to interfere with its success, so there are no hard and fast rules about when and where it will work and where it won't. But from time to time conditions do interfere. The following are common problems that are easily corrected. If you find that EFT isn't working—that is, you or the person you're working with experience no change and the situation seems stuck —try these remedies.

1. **There may be a problem with energy in the room,** or you may be exposed to an energy toxin. Try going outside or into another room. There are many possible sources of electromagnetic interference, including fluorescent lighting. Try changing rooms or going outside. Take several deep breaths, really filling your lungs. Then try your Setup and tapping sequence again.

2. **Maybe it's something you ate.** A few years ago I worked with a woman who had suffered major bouts of depression since age nine. When I first met her, Louella was suicidal. Tears came easily and "hopeless" seemed to be her favorite word. EFT tapping helped, but whenever her depression lifted a little, it came right back—and this continued after we found and treated several core issues, relieving her back pain and asthma along the way.

    During our sixth partially successful session, she felt better until she ate an apple. Within minutes she was on the brink of a panic attack, her depression shot back to a 10, she acted as though she had taken a drug, and she fell asleep for several hours.

We invented a "detective diet" to establish what other foods might be causing her problem. She agreed to eat only organic foods (the apple that put her to sleep was not organically grown), eat one food at a time, and wait one hour between foods.

From the moment Louella started this detective diet, her depression began to lift, and within 24 hours it completely disappeared. She slept normally, went on long hikes with friends, enjoyed dancing again, and vacationed in Spain. She learned to avoid wheat, which was the only organic food that triggered an adverse reaction. As long as she stayed away from wheat and commercially grown fruits and vegetables, she felt terrific.

Louella's food sensitivities are not unusual. Many holistic physicians routinely recommend that their patients stop eating common allergens, like wheat and dairy products, and in many cases their health improves right away.

Many EFTers notice that when they eat certain foods, they soon feel tired, their memory declines, simple projects seem suddenly complicated, and even the most basic EFT tapping requires exhausting effort. In fact, many forget all about EFT. Responses to food are individual, but many experience this kind of fatigue soon after they eat sweets and simple carbohydrates. In addition to keeping a food diary, those familiar with Applied Kinesiology can use muscle testing to check for food sensitivities.

3. **Try varying the Setup.** Try switching from the Karate Chop point to the Sore Spot for your set-up phrase, or vice versa.

4. **You may not know what to tap for.** This is not unusual, especially for beginners. It's hard to know what issue to choose, which detail to select, or how to address an issue once you find it. Your subconscious mind can be your ally here. Try using a Setup that invites the subconscious mind to communicate, such as:

> *"Even though I don't know how to use EFT for this problem, I know that my imagination will come up with an appropriate phrase."*

> *"Even though I don't know how to define this problem, the right words will come to me without effort."*

5. **You may need to do more repetitions.** I often say that the secrets to success with EFT are focus and perseverance. As long as you experience at least some improvement, you are moving in the right direction. EFT practitioners and students often report that when they felt stuck, going nowhere, but continued to tap and tap and tap—suddenly everything shifted.

6. **You may be avoiding unhappy memories.** Some people feel uncomfortable saying negative Setups. They're afraid that thinking about a problem will make it worse. This fear is actually a wonderful tapping subject. By focusing on their fear of tapping, many EFT novices have jumped straight to core

issues with excellent results. Example: *I don't want to tap on my weight problem.* There's your opportunity! Start tapping on:

> *Even though I don't want to tap on my weight problem, it makes me uncomfortable, I'd rather not even think about it, I don't want to do this, I don't want to think about _____, and I definitely don't want to remember _____.*

Let your mind fill in the blanks. Unhappy memories are what make EFT work. Welcome those unhappy memories and start tapping.

EFT is not designed to be a painful procedure. Just tap and think about an unhappy event from a distance, then move a little closer. If it begins to feel painful, back up and tap until the feeling subsides. Then continue. Thanks to EFT tapping, you won't have to relive the experience. You can observe it from a distance without being emotionally involved. This step-by-step procedure, which we call the Tearless Trauma Technique, has freed EFTers of all ages from the shackles of painful memories while neutralizing core issues that created their pain and discomfort.

7. **Try tapping more often.** Try to tap at least five times a day—and more often when you think of it. Set a tapping goal, such as tapping every hour on the hour or at a certain time of day. Tap while you read this book. Find a tapping buddy, someone who can tap with you in person or on the phone, and tap with that person at every opportunity. Recruit friends or

family members to form a tapping group. Tap while you watch TV. Tap while you walk the dog. Tap before every meal, whenever you use the bathroom, and whenever you take a bath or shower. Serious EFTers are ingenious about creating time to tap throughout the day.

8. **Look for new perspectives.** Always try to find a new way of looking at an old, stuck issue. Approach your problem from new directions. Involve your imagination. Think of the problem as a play or movie and put your favorite actors in the cast. Think of it as a computer game and visualize its special effects. Go back to the Personal Peace Procedure (see page 150) and work through a dozen different issues.

9. **Watch yourself in a mirror as you tap.** As Carol Look notes on page 194, mirror tapping is an excellent way to discover phrases and statements that make you feel uncomfortable. For example, some are able to say "I fully and completely accept and love myself" if they're looking at a wall but not if they're looking at themselves in a mirror. Once EFT neutralizes negative emotions and you install positive emotions and affirmations in their place, mirror tapping can strengthen those positive results, making them a more powerful part of you.

10. **Shout it out!** If the set-up phrase isn't getting through, you may not be saying it loudly enough. In many of my seminars, I've had people *shout* their set-up phrases. Some people do this in their cars with the radio volume turned up. Others do it in the

shower. To involve your entire being in this exercise, use emphatic gestures or jump up and down.

11. **Get some vigorous exercise.** There's a definite connection between the lymph system and the body's energy system. When you're sedentary, lymph doesn't circulate, so the body's waste removal slows down, and that interferes with not only EFT but your overall health and thought processes. Some exciting EFT results have been achieved immediately after a vigorous physical workout.

12. **Clear your energy.** Donna Eden, author of the best seller *Energy Medicine* and co-author (with David Feinstein and me) of *The Promise of Energy Psychology,* has taught thousands how to clear their energy and keep it balanced with tapping and other exercises. See any of Donna's books or videos for instructions.

9

Terrorist Attacks and
Other Nightmares

Civilian populations are affected by natural and man-made disasters even more than military populations are. Unlike military personnel, police, and rescue workers, most people haven't received any training or experience that would help them anticipate or cope with the aftermath of terrible events. Fortunately, EFT tapping can fill that void. Here is how some EFT practitioners helped themselves and others deal with the unexpected.

One week after the 2001 attacks on the World Trade Center in New York City, Dr. Carol Look, whose office is two miles away, shared the following suggestions for traumatized therapists and details about the escape of a traumatized client. Throughout her report you will find helpful insights and language for use with yourself and others.

EFT and the Aftermath of 9/11

by Dr. Carol Look

Many of the survivors who worked until last week in the World Trade Center have been experiencing the classic cluster of symptoms of Post-Traumatic Stress Disorder, including auditory and visual flashbacks, an exaggerated startle response, nightmares, profound restlessness and a heightened state of agitation. I would like to address the population of people experiencing a milder, scaled down version of PTSD. While their symptoms are less severe than those of people who barely escaped with their lives, they are still unbearable and deserve and require competent treatment.

Some of those New Yorkers who did not lose direct family members are experiencing deep grief as a result of being glued to the news accounts of the tragedy and from seeing hundreds of photograph posters of the missing that make the loss of complete strangers all the more personal. They are also grieving the symbol of downtown, the buildings that represented the commerce of the country. They can't get away from the constant sound of sirens, day and night, the smell of smoke and destruction, and the look of terror on neighbors' faces. Friends and clients are unsettled in the present, afraid of the future and "unhinged" by last week's attack.

The most prevalent emotional symptoms for people suffering in this second tier of PTSD include feelings of guilt, helplessness and anxiety. In addition, I have observed signs of distraction (people staring at you but not hearing what you are saying), emotional numbness (shock), mild disorientation (getting into the shower with socks or glasses on), irritability (picking fights with loved ones), losing orientation to time and space (missing important meetings/ bumping into things), and being dissociated from feelings and events. Strong feelings of "survivor's guilt" are preventing individuals from validating or expressing their feelings, and a strong sense of feeling unsafe is preventing people from making wise, centered decisions in their daily lives. These emotional states and their oppressive consequences can be efficiently handled with EFT.

Suggestions for a Traumatized Therapist

It is not just weekly clients who feel disoriented, exhausted, frustrated and traumatized. Therapists are, of course, among those New Yorkers who need help. Hundreds of mental health workers have lost patients and loved ones or witnessed the devastation directly, yet they expect themselves to be ready and emotionally available to comfort others. Numerous colleagues have been telling me that they feel as if they went back to work too early.

Many described feeling stunned and unprepared for hearing the horror stories and fears of their clients, one after another, all day long. One social worker said she was overwhelmed by her patients' actual experiences. Several of her clients had waited until feeling surrounded by the safety of their therapist's office to tell every last detail of the catastrophe.

Still other colleagues said they were under the impression that they were coping well and processing what had happened until stories of unprecedented devastation were recounted in their offices. Colleagues are telling me they are going to work without their appointment books, double booking their sessions, making poor logistical decisions, failing to carry out routine chores, and feeling empty, lonely, helpless and afraid. One therapist told me she felt useless as a professional and was "leaking" her own emotions all over the place.

As mental health professionals, we must be able to take care of ourselves in order to offer comfort and care to others. When I volunteered at the Armory for the families who were directed there to report missing loved ones, numerous mental health workers appeared nearly as traumatized and disoriented as the family members. Some social workers were so eager to "help" that they were emotionally intrusive and missed important clues from the distressed families.

Some of the most effective EFT practitioners I know "forgot" to seek help or treat themselves and only compounded their feelings of distress by volunteering too long or going back to work too soon. A seasoned clinician told me he feared he had added to the emotional damage of his clients by being too distraught himself to be present.

Here are some useful Setup phrases for over-whelmed therapists:

"Even though I don't want to hear about it any-more..."

"Even though my clients' fears scare me...and I feel overwhelmed..."

"Even though I shouldn't want to protect myself from the stories..."

"Even though I should be doing more...helping more" (*"I am enough...I do enough..."*)

"Even though I resent their neediness when I have my own needs..."

"Even though I'm mad at her for telling me the grue-some details..." (*"I wish I hadn't heard that story..."*)

"Even though I want to be taken care of instead of taking care of them..."

"Even though I feel guilty...I should be able to handle this..."

"Even though I'm afraid of the hatred I'm hearing about...I choose love..."

"Even though I wasn't afraid of the future until they reminded me to be..."

"Even though I feel helpless and powerless...I want to feel safe..."

"Even though I can't stop seeing the images in my head..."

Treatment for a Client Who Escaped

I wanted to share a portion of the treatment process I used with a client who felt guilty and unsafe as a result of last week's devastation:

This morning I worked with Jen who had been attending a meeting in a building directly across the street from the World Trade Center when the attack occurred. She escaped through a southern entrance of the building, was covered in soot, and crawled under a fence with other employees to safety at the tip of the island. Jen has a sketchy memory of the morning, and she told me she was in "survivor mode" all day, blocking her feelings of fear and vulnerability. It was quite evident she had been traumatized.

First we tapped for...

"Even though I still feel jittery, and scared of the future..."

"Even though I don't feel safe in New York anymore..." and

"Even though I can't believe I went through that incident..."

"Even though I feel threatened...I can and do take care of myself..."

At various treatment spots I alternated *"I feel safe now"* with *"I'm not safe"* until Jen calmed down. (Please note that using the "Tell a Story" technique is also very helpful. The clients are already tuned in and just narrate what happened *("and then...and then...*

and then…") while they tap on themselves or you tap on them).

We then turned to Jen's feelings of guilt. She described herself as "fine" and not nearly as traumatized as other people who lost their loved ones. She felt guilty about receiving attention and help. She said she felt overwhelmed by the enormity of the problem, even aware that I, her therapist, must be going through trauma. Jen also felt wracked with guilt because she had burst into hysterical giggles and laughter Friday evening. She felt totally out of balance, although she enjoyed and needed the release. With EFT, Jen was able to reframe her outburst as a natural release of intense emotion, rather than humor that she feared offended others.

"Even though I shouldn't have been laughing…"

"Even though I feel guilty for being upset…when I wasn't hurt as much as others…"

"Even though I shouldn't get the attention…others deserve it more than I…"

"Even though I feel guilty getting on with my life…I choose to take care of my needs…"

"Even though I feel guilty for not doing more…for wanting to change the subject…"

These rounds produced a deeper awareness of guilt and physical feelings in her chest and throat which needed attention.

"Even though I have this heaviness in my chest…the dust and the screams…"

"Even though I have this anxiety in my throat...I'm afraid to stay in New York..."

"Even though the future is so uncertain...and I'm afraid of what is going to happen..."

"Even though I'm afraid I'm in denial..." (People kept telling her she was in denial and would fall apart in the near future.)

Jen described feeling deeply conflicted between two sets of experiences and feelings:

1. feelings of shock and terror when in her downtown home where she compulsively watched the news around the clock, and

2. feelings of relief she felt when working uptown in Manhattan where she found people seemingly oblivious to it all—with an absence of reminders such as candlelight vigils or hospitals teaming with families and people in crisis. She wasn't sure which emotional state was "right" or appropriate.

"Even though I don't know where I fit in...nothing feels stable any more..."

"Even though I feel guilty for wanting to run away..."

"Even though I don't want to burden other people with my fears..."

"Even though I don't know how to react...I choose to love and accept myself anyway."

"Even though I need a break from it all...I accept all of me..."

We kept tapping until Jen regained the confidence in her own ability to handle what she had experienced.

❊ ❊ ❊

In this next report, Rebecca Marina offers this firsthand account of a successful EFT treatment for the trauma experienced by one survivor.

EFT for a Hurricane Katrina Survivor

by Rebecca Marina

It is important to pre-frame this story by telling you that Paulette is a very gifted intuitive healer and medium. She knew something was coming to New Orleans but she refused to "see." She felt devastated that she was no longer in a position to help others because of her own extreme emotional trauma.

Paulette lived only five blocks from the Mighty Mississippi in downtown New Orleans. She heard Katrina was coming and, like so many others, fled reluctantly. She took only the bare minimum thinking she would be back in two or three days. Here is her story.

At the beginning of our phone session, Paulette was almost hysterical and exhausted from her ordeal. She felt hopeless, abandoned, betrayed, and very angry at people for criticizing the officials in New Orleans. Worse, she doubted that she could ever do her work again. She felt as if she had absolutely nothing left in this world.

I asked Paulette to tell me a little of her story so we could address her most pressing emotions first. Paulette could hardly talk. She rated her level of anxiety and confusion at a 10 and reported feeling foggy, numb, hopeless, disconnected, displaced, and angry.

We began by addressing her feelings of being displaced, confused, and foggy headed.

Even though I feel so confused, my life is upside down, and I don't know what to do…

Even though I don't understand why this had to happen to me…

Even though I don't understand why this sneaked up on me, I refused to "see" this coming…

I release this fear that has gotten hold of me…

I've always been the strong one, it's hard for me to ask for help…

I can't help anyone else now and I don't know what to do…

I am afraid I won't be able to help anyone and I won't be able to do my work…

When we re-checked Paulette's intensity on "confusion," she felt it was a 6. I should have asked how she knew it was a 6 because Paulette became distracted and started talking about how angry she felt that the media was criticizing the mayor of New Orleans so much.

She started to get very emotional and I had Paulette tap on herself while telling me the story.

"Tell a Story" is a wonderful technique for dissolving emotions. Just tap while talking about the situation or event that bothers you.

When Paulette was a bit calmer, I told her we would "harness the power" of her anger. I explained that anger, used properly, can help transform negative to positive in very short order.

I asked Paulette to give me some details of why she felt angry and we had some great set up phrases in:

Even though I feel so angry at the media for criticizing the mayor—at least he didn't leave—I love and accept myself.

Even though I feel so angry at the Red Cross and the Salvation Army for selling clothes, buy one get one free, I love and accept myself.

Even though I feel so angry I could just scream [and she did scream a few choice words] I deeply love and accept myself.

We then stopped and Paulette said she now felt great! I asked her to re-check the original emotion of confusion and it was down to none at all.

We then tapped in some positive choices using Dr Carrington's Choices phrasing and Paulette became more calm, centered, and ready to pick up the pieces and move forward. The difference was just incredible.

❀ ❀ ❀

10

Advanced
Work with Veterans

Lindsay Kenny is an experienced EFT practitioner who participated in our March 2008 event in San
Francisco. Here, for the benefit of counselors and practitioners, she describes a simple EFT approach that is
highly effective for complex and challenging PTSD cases
—and, as she notes, it can also help those who want to try
EFT on their own.

Tapping for Collections of Traumas

by Lindsay Kenny

During the week of working with combat veterans in San Francisco, I was struck by childhood
issues that the veterans shared. I worked with nine of
the eleven participants and I don't think there was a
single one who didn't have significant baggage from
childhood. It occurred to me that they were attracted
to military service because it gave structure to their
lives. A lot of them had repressive, domineering,

dictatorial, judgmental, critical parents, which is interesting when you consider the behavior of most drill sergeants and commanding officers.

The veterans who have the most difficult time, I think, are those who experience terrible things all their lives, in childhood, during the war, and after they come home. Unhappy events get layered on top of each other until the person reaches a breaking point. I call this "piling on." When someone goes on a shooting spree or has a total breakdown, it's never because of a single event. It's one thing after another until it's like the straw that breaks the camel's back and the person just snaps.

In the first session with each of the nine veterans I worked with in San Francisco, I started with the long-ago past. Each of the participants had completed a personal history and in preparation for the EFT sessions, we read about events in their lives that were shocking. Rather than focusing on recent events, I started each session by asking the person about things that happened in childhood, the first traumas that he or she experienced. This was an effective way to introduce EFT, and it also established rapport.

The participants could see that EFT worked, that it could help them get over some serious issues painlessly and that they could trust us. It was also a sensible place to start because a lot of them weren't ready to talk about their war experiences. It was a way of establishing a foundation or background, which is what I do whenever I'm teaching EFT. Start with your childhood, start with the very old traumas, and then you can sneak up on current problems.

The veterans dealt with their most serious traumas in different ways. Some just stated what happened, like "I had to watch my best friend get blown up and then I had to pick up his arms and legs and put them in a body bag" as if they were reading a phone number. In those cases I started right in on the event's different aspects and their intensity, the sights, smells, and sounds, and finally the actual events themselves. Once the remembered sights, smells, and sounds generated less intensity, that's when I dealt with their emotions: the grief, anger, betrayal, frustration, and that sort of thing.

In PTSD counseling, if the person can talk about a trauma and name it, that's an effective way to proceed. That's very different from the approach you have to take with people who don't want to talk about what happened. They may say, "I'm afraid to bring it up, I've got it buried, I don't want to think about it."

In EFT we have gentle ways of sneaking up on problems, like the Tearless Trauma Technique. You don't have to describe the details of a specific problem to get good results. You can give it a title like "That Summer Night" or "The Afternoon in Baghdad," and that's all you have to say. You can tap to defuse the emotion and gradually peel away the layers before you ever get to the specifics.

For most of the veterans, the problem wasn't one single event, it was a series of events, several different things. I like to collect these before we begin by bundling together a series of negative repetitive events that are similar or related, which in this case include things like bombs going off, sounds of gunfire, people disappearing, watching people die, seeing collections of body parts, and other horrific things.

I would say, "Just imagine, without thinking of any specific events, all those times that you were traumatized during the war, hearing gunfire at night, hearing bombs go off, and having friends not come back. Put all of those events together without focusing on any one of them, just put them in a bundle and give the bundle a name, like 'Horrific War Trauma' or 'My Nightmare in Afghanistan.' Now, if you allowed yourself to get upset, but don't go there, what do you guess your level of intensity would be on a scale from zero to 10?"

It was always a 10, or some would say it's a 20. Then we would tap that whole collective bundle of trauma down to a low number, at which point the person would often say something like, "You know, what really bothers me is the time I found my friend's finger with his college ring on it," or some specific memory that really bothered him or her. We would then move from the general to the specific while the person remained relaxed and comfortable.

One huge thing that stood out to me, which they all experienced in the service, was a horrific sense of betrayal. They all felt betrayed by a superior officer, by their branch of the service, by their country, or by someone or some thing. This got layered onto whatever other betrayals they had already experienced in life.

The anger that they held onto often kept a trauma alive. They wanted to keep that anger and that sense of betrayal in order to keep alive thoughts about punishing whoever or whatever they were mad at. That's like drinking poison and hoping the person you're mad at gets sick or dies. But it was very hard for them to imagine any other way of responding until we tapped on the issue. Then, in most cases, the sense of betrayal and all the emotional intensity that went with it disappeared in a single session.

Each session was an hour and 15 minutes long, and often we would deal with more than one issue during a session. Everyone had problems with stress, anxiety, insomnia, night sweats, night terrors, TMJ (Temporo-Mandibular Joint problems) from clenching the jaw, or tinnitus, which is a ringing in the ears. Not all of them had seen actual combat. One participant got PTSD just from being in the service but not in a war, complete with anxiety, night sweats, paranoia, insomnia, TMJ, and pain. Others had PTSD from having family members in the service.

Every morning we reviewed the participants' progress by going over the list of what we had worked with the day before or in previous sessions, asking general questions like, "How are you doing with insomnia? Were you able to sleep last night?" The usual reply was, "I got a great night's sleep, the best sleep I've had in 30 years." Then we'd go to the next item on the list, like TMJ or tension in the neck, checking on each physical symptom and making note of its improvement.

Of the nine vets I worked with in San Francisco using this method, all experienced significant improvement. They went through tremendous changes in their attitudes, their outlook on life, and how they felt about themselves.

I worked with one woman who was the mother of one of the vets. She came in with symptoms that were very similar to her son's, and was able to quickly collapse all of them. After the first day, when she went from a 10 to a zero on 15 to 20 separate issues, we really didn't have anything for her to do. She was in a very happy mode.

It was absolutely astonishing to see someone cringing and walking with short, uncomfortable steps while struggling down the hall with a tense scowl on his face and anger permeating out of every cell, avoiding eye contact with everyone, then seeing the same person two or three days later striding confidently with a smile on his face, joking with the other participants, happy, walking upright, and looking people in the eye.

When these guys first arrived, they were tense with each other and with themselves, and their attitude toward us was so hostile that we were a little afraid. By the end of the week, they all went out to dinner together and were laughing, joking, and having such a great time that they were asked to tone it down. You would never have known that this was the same group of traumatized people who had been tense, isolated, and miserable just a few days before.

To keep track of their progress, in addition to noting their test scores, I kept in email contact with everyone I worked with for several weeks. I made sure they were doing okay and reminded them of things they planned to work on. A lot of them had projects they wanted to start, jobs they wanted to get, and in other ways move their lives in a new direction. Their physical symptoms were better, too, everything from TMJ and tinnitus to insomnia and arthritis pain or headaches. In fact, the symptoms weren't just better, they were gone.

Some of these people had to go back into situations that were difficult, such as with their families or their jobs, so they still had to deal with stress or anxiety, but after relieving themselves of substantial pain, trauma, and negativity, they re-entered those situations with a clean slate. They weren't reacting the way they did in the past. They dealt with current problems at a much different level. They were calmer, more focused, had more clarity of thought and more confidence. Most importantly, they did it without spending months, years, or even decades in therapy or on medications.

One of the vets was a woman who was taking care of two parents with Alzheimer's. They were abusive and demanding of her time, and when she came in, she was very stressed—plus, in the service, she had been abused, molested, and raped twice. Her situation was really difficult. Yet now, after the tapping, the situation with her parents is much easier to deal with. It's not getting to her the way it used to. She's handling it more calmly and with confidence, and she uses EFT to dispel problems as they come up.

When dealing with any highly charged issue, past or chronic events or issues, you can eliminate subconscious resistance to change by tapping on the Karate Chop point while saying three times:

*Even though I **don't** want to let go of these problems [naming the collective name or individual issue], I want to love and accept who I am.*

By addressing and neutralizing that subconscious resistance head-on, the EFT process go much more easily and quickly. After doing the reversal neutralization you just go into normal EFT.

Then you can move from the distant past to the more recent past, and then move to the present. In each of these time frames, think of a general theme and all the events or memories that are connected to it and give it a name. Tap on that general theme until the intensity level falls to a more comfortable level. Then collect all the emotions you feel about those events and tap in a general way on those. I believe, based on my experience, that it's safer to deal with events first and then emotions.

Many people feel overwhelmed by a sense of having everything go wrong in life—they're in pain or don't feel well physically, they're in the middle of a divorce, they're facing a layoff at work, they're behind on the mortgage, and wherever they look, they see problems. When stressful events mount up, I have people write everything down so that all those problems are on a single piece of paper. When I ask them to give it a name, they'll say something like "My Hellish Life" or "This Nightmare" or "Being Overwhelmed." We tap on the list's title using a Setup such as:

> *Even though I have this nightmare life and I'm feeling overwhelmed, I love and accept myself.*

Then we tap the EFT points using the title as the reminder phrase: *My nightmare life, my nightmare life, my nightmare life...*

I think it's very difficult for most people to deal with complex issues like PTSD on their own even if they are experienced with EFT. It's a lot easier with the help of a trained, skilled professional who can guide them through it. That being said, there are people who will want to try EFT on their own, either by preference or necessity, and when they do, I believe it will help them to take this collective approach, to start by focusing not on individual events but on a collection of related events and to give the collection a name and tap on it until its intensity level drops. This is the opposite of what we normally do with EFT, but for the treatment of PTSD and other complex issues, this is a safe approach, and it works.

❊ ❊ ❊

EFT coach Ingrid Dinter spends considerable time working with veterans, and her gentle expertise provides an excellent model for counselors and practitioners who use EFT to help not only military personnel but police, emergency medical technicians, hospital staff, fire fighters, and all who have been trained to keep their feelings from interfering with their professional responsibilities. Ingrid combines general rather than specific Setups with constantly changing Reminder Phrases, all of which help clients relax, feel comfortable, and eventually reveal core issues. In this comprehensive report, she takes us step by step through the EFT counseling process. Ingrid used these same techniques at our 2008 PTSD conference with excellent results.

Introducing EFT to Combat Veterans

by Ingrid Dinter

Since I don't want new clients to get unnecessarily upset, I try not to ask too many war-related questions before I introduce EFT. Instead, we tap a few rounds on general issues, which helps the person relax. It is usually easier to explain EFT after the client has tried it and seen results.

I like to start with a round of tapping on feeling overwhelmed, as this is usually appropriate and shows respect for the client and his or her emotions. It can also help to take the edge off in a safe and comfortable way and set the stage for more tapping.

Even though I feel very overwhelmed right now, I allow myself to be surprisingly okay with that.

This set up statement usually startles people, as it feels appropriate. They usually feel more relaxed, less apprehensive, and often even experience physical relief—and we were not specific, and it didn't hurt.

The word "surprisingly" opens us up to receiving new solutions and new feelings, even if we are not aware of them yet. Being open to positive surprises can fill us with expectations and curiosity, allowing us to consider new ways of dealing with our past, ways that we didn't even know were possible before.

Another statement that I use a lot is:

Even though I have been through more than you will ever understand, I choose to be surprisingly at peace with that.

Any way of phrasing this basic statement is appropriate, such as:

Even though I have been through more than anyone knows or can understand, I choose to be surprisingly okay with that.

After each round of tapping, in which I encourage the client to change any phrasing so it works better, the result can be greater trust and more relaxation. The client now sees that he or she is in control. With each round of EFT, I fill in the explanations and information the soldier needs to understand how and why we are so successful releasing trauma in a gentle, fast and non-traumatizing way.

Even though I don't want to make a fool of myself by tapping on my head and body, I choose to allow myself to relax about it.

Even though I could quite easily get very emotional here and I don't want that, I choose to feel surprisingly safe and in control.

Even though I have been through more than anybody will ever understand, I choose to allow myself to heal in a way that works for me.

Even though I am overwhelmed by all that I have been through, and the mere thought of it is scary, I choose to feel confident that I can take it one step at a time, in a way that works for me.

If the veteran feels angry about the offer to help, which can be a side effect of PTSD, trust issues, or not completely establishing rapport, but wants to give it just one shot:

Even though I resent the thought of even considering peace, healing or forgiveness, and only veterans can understand why I am saying this and you just don't know what you are talking about, I allow myself to feel respected for all that I have been through, and I consider the possibility that I can find and accept healing in a way that works for me.

Even though _____, I allow myself to consider the possibility that I can feel safe enough to relax about it…

Even though _____, I consider being as relaxed as I was when I was when I was fifteen…

Even though _____, I choose to find it surprisingly appropriate to find peace anyway…

A longer, more carefully "testing the waters" version could be:

Even though _____, I allow myself to consider that there is a way that allows me to be at peace with this in a way that works for me and everybody else involved.

And finally:

Even though _____, I choose to claim my power back in a way that feels safe and appropriate.

In my experience, veterans often don't like to talk and bring up memories that we could work on. They have a wall around themselves that keeps them safe and required some huge effort to build. As an EFT practitioner, I find it important to recognize and accept the wall for as long as the soldier needs it, as it gives a feeling of control and safety. At the same time, there are feelings and mindsets that many soldiers share. Those may include feelings of being overwhelmed, misunderstood, or cheated.

Life isn't fair.

I am angry all the time.

My life is like never waking up from a bad dream.

People see me as a monster.

I feel like a failure.

I'm not able to keep my family or others safe.

I am not safe for others to be around.

My marriage is in trouble.

My buddy got killed and I couldn't help him.

My physical health is deteriorating.

I have pain where there shouldn't be pain.

I am injured and they told me that I will never recover.

I hate authority.

I am always on guard and never feel safe.

I don't trust anyone.

I suffer from insomnia.

I have intrusive thoughts.

And the list goes on. If it is safe and appropriate, it can be very healing to ask for a specific event that caused any of these feelings, beliefs, or physical symptoms, and let the soldier choose which one he wants to tap on.

In my experience, when a veteran has suffered for so long from guilt, shame, and self blame, an excuse, no matter how well intentioned, will be hard to accept. It may even increase the person's negative self-talk, that what happened was so bad that there is indeed no way to ever receive forgiveness unless we make something up. Instead, It can help to listen calmly and respectfully for the soldier's version of the situation. Tapping on each component of it, using the

Movie Technique and Tearless Trauma Technique, can release excess feelings about what happened. I often see that there was more to the story than what the soldier remembered or found important, and in those details we often find the true reason for what happened and why.

War has rules and a life of its own. Once a soldier becomes a part of war, he may be exposed to situations that force him to make decisions that he later regrets.

Here are some setups that might help bring relief:

Even though war sucks, and so did my role in it, I can't believe what it made me do, and I feel guilty and responsible for the things that happened, I choose to allow myself to find peace with that in an appropriate way that truly works for me, the victims, and everybody else involved.

Even though it hurts to see what war has made of me and my dreams and values, and I feel ashamed about the whole thing, I choose to allow myself to find peace and forgiveness in surprising and appropriate ways.

Even though I wish this had never happened, and I can't forgive myself for what I have done, I choose to allow myself to heal from what war has made of me and find a better way to honor and support those who had to suffer through what happened.

Even though I can't imagine my life will ever be what it was before I left, I choose to open up to the possibility that there are ways to live a powerful, meaningful life in a way that truly works for me and those I care for.

Finding Meaning

Many vets feel that they have a lesson to teach but suffer too much or don't feel comfortable enough to share their story or even consider being heard. Opening up that possibility can help them find power in their past:

Even though I believe that the guilt that I have felt for all these years will never be enough to make up for what happened or for what I did, I open up to the possibility that there might be a more powerful way of taking responsibility for what happened and transforming it into a powerful lesson of peace.

Even though I am sorry for what I did, and I could never express it, I allow myself now to realize that my plea for forgiveness might be heard, even by myself.

Then we do a round of tapping using Reminder Phrases like "I'm sorry for what happened" and, "I ask for forgiveness and I allow myself to receive it."

❊ ❊ ❊

11

PTSD Complications

There are many theories about the causes of Post-Traumatic Stress Disorder and its complications.

For example, if terrible things happen in childhood, these events are said to produce dissociation and brain changes that make the adult personality more likely to suffer from acute PTSD and require special treatment. I don't doubt that childhood traumas contribute to PTSD, but this theory is simply a way to explain a condition that I explain differently.

When we deal with combat veterans and others who have gone through significant traumas, I believe we are dealing with two basic levels of experience.

First, there is the level that involves what happened during the war, and this level includes the traumatic events themselves plus all the intrusive memories, nightmares, things they can't let go of, and other symptoms that occur thereafter. The same is true for traumatic events that disrupt civilian life.

The second level is one in which newer memories build upon older memories, including those from childhood. I describe the older memories as foundational because they create a supporting structure on which newer memories are layered.

To give you an example, in my work with serious diseases, I dealt with a veteran named John. When I first talked with John on the phone, he could not say my name. This is because a soldier named Gary was killed after John sent him with radio equipment to the front lines in battle. John felt so massively guilty about this that he couldn't talk about it, couldn't think about it, and couldn't mention the fellow's name, even when it belonged to someone entirely different, like myself.

We could deal with this memory quite logically by discussing how he had to send someone to deliver the equipment because if he didn't, the whole battalion could go down. And we could have tapped on different aspects of this situation, such as Gary being his friend, the shock he felt when Gary died, and so forth. But what we found once we got into the session was that when John was growing up, his father embedded in him this immense feeling of being responsible for everything.

So, years later, he sent someone to his death, and he felt responsible. It was his feeling of responsibility that was the real issue. Where did that feeling come from? It came from his father's repeated statements, reminders, and lectures. This is what I call "the writings on your walls" (see page 173) rather than dissociation, a disturbance of mental function, temporal lobe damage, or anything else.

When you get back to what happened in the past that created the writings on your walls, you begin unraveling the situation at its most basic level. Yes, you have to clear the trauma from the war incident, but you're going to do a more thorough job, assuming you are an accomplished EFTer who is skilled in asking the right questions, by going back to the underlying issues, the original or core issues, that created the problem in the first place.

I agree with those who consider PTSD to be a complex condition, because in many cases it is. But what I find interesting is that we have so many one-minute wonders and one-session wonders when using EFT for war trauma, even among combat veterans who have multiple problems and multiple traumas, not to mention years of psychotherapy and other conventional treatments. These are people whose entire traumatic memory and all of its aspects and results disappear in a few minutes, never to return. You'll see examples of this in our "Six Days at the V.A." DVD, and I saw many more in San Francisco at our PTSD study.

Combat veterans often have multiple issues, so as soon as the person feels comfortable describing the past, I take it one specific event at a time. That remains my favorite way of tackling any condition, not just PTSD. At the same time, I have to pay close attention to the person's comfort level. EFT is not a treatment that requires anyone to suffer, to climb back into an unhappy past event and relive it. You don't have to do that. This is why we often spend time skirting around or "sneaking up on" big issues, and we get close to them only when the person feels comfortable. The Tearless Trauma Technique is described on page 155, and it's the procedure I recommend for all trauma cases.

In my approach to PTSD, you start with the general and, as soon as the person feels comfortable, you move to the specific. As soon as the person feels uncomfortable telling the story or even thinking about a specific thing that happened, you step back from the event and tap until the feeling of emotional intensity falls to a zero. Only then do you continue with the story or approach it in the first place.

In our San Francisco group, I worked with a veteran who had one horrific memory which he described as "behind a wall," and he said that no one was ever going to see it.

I started by spending five to eight minutes treating this memory globally, that is, in a very general and non-specific way, just to take the edges off, with statements like:

> *Even though I've had all these experiences, I fully and completely accept myself.*

That's all it took for him to decide to tell his story. I was startled because I had planned to spend the better part of an hour sneaking up on the issue. I said, "Wait a minute, you're telling the story already," to which he replied, "Yes, I am, and don't stop me."

So I sat back and listened as he talked. When he finished, he was ashen-faced and felt nauseated, and he had to leave for a few minutes. When he came back he still looked pale and queasy. We then did 10 to 15 minutes of

EFT tapping using the descriptions he had just given me, creating Setups like:

> *Even though I kept pulling body parts out of the rubble, like two feet that had been blown off…*

We kept tapping on it and tapping on it until he was able to tell the story with no emotional intensity whatsoever. The next day I tapped with him while we tested the different aspects of the story and collapsed the whole thing. By collapse, I mean that we completely neutralized every aspect of the entire episode so that there wasn't a single thought, memory, reminder, or part of the event that triggered any emotional intensity, even when Bob concentrated hard on the worst images.

To my knowledge, this veteran did not have any foundational events, such as things that happened in childhood, that contributed to his battle-related PTSD. If he had, I could have taken any one specific event or scene and tapped on it while keeping his attention on it until it was neutralized. The secret here is tapping on one event at a time, without shifting to other scenes or events, until the emotional charge is gone.

In our San Francisco study, quite a few of the participants had foundational issues, problems that were built on problems going back years or decades, and these problems manifested in different ways, including alcohol abuse and difficult living conditions. It wasn't possible in those five days to take care of everything for everyone, but the progress we made was startling.

I don't have statistical studies to back this up, but it's been my observation that with 80 to 90 percent of these traumatic memories—and I don't care how horrible they are—if you just keep tapping and focusing on one specific event and all its pieces and stay on that event, you will likely collapse it, even by yourself.

If someone is not able to focus on an event that occurred in adulthood, the chances are that it's bouncing off of a childhood issue. Someone working by himself or herself might not be able to discern that, which is why EFT works best for PTSD if you are working with an experienced practitioner who can help you stay on topic.

But even if you don't have access to an experienced EFT practitioner, I'm convinced that EFT can help you if you use common sense, start with general statements that set the stage and help you relax, then tap on the smallest and least scary memory or event that bothers you in any way, really focus on that one event, and keep tapping.

I call this the "divide and conquer" approach. Our subconscious minds lump all kinds of memories together. What we want to do is separate these memories into specific events, preferably small or inconsequential ones first, so that we get used to collapsing our emotional connection to past events. This not only helps us anticipate the positive changes that tapping will bring to other issues but it actually strengthens us by balancing our energy and keeping it balanced. Remember that every negative emotion and most of our physical symptoms stem from an imbalance in the body's energy system. When our energy is out of balance, we are far more likely to expect the worst, but when our energy is balanced, we are far more likely to expect the best and act accordingly.

By starting with smaller, less important traumas, we set the stage for success with larger, more important issues. However, I recommend that you consult a professional if matters become intense. EFT is a remarkable do-it-yourself tool, but it must be used with common sense.

Abreactions and Dissociation

In World War I and other wars of the late 19th and early 20th Centuries, the terms "shell shock" and "combat fatigue" described soldiers whose lives were permanently altered by traumatic memories. The same terms were applied to Prisoners of War and survivors of natural disasters and other traumas.

Sigmund Freud created the term "abreaction" to describe the way severely traumatized people relive their most frightening experiences. By World War II, psychologists were experimenting with therapies that encouraged combat veterans and others to relive past events in a safe and controlled environment. Abreactions—or the reliving of those past events—became an important part of the treatment. In fact, in some cases, reliving the past in intense detail was the only treatment. Even today, several therapeutic approaches to PTSD consider abreactions a critical element in the healing process.

But abreactions are painful. They generate flashbacks that are psychologically difficult and physically painful. In some clinics, patients were tied down or physically restrained prior to treatment so that they wouldn't injure themselves or staff members when they re-experienced the sights, sounds, smells, and sensations that haunted them.

Abreactions are not the goal of EFT. If they do occur, EFT is a fist-aid treatment that often brings the person back to the present moment as quickly and comfortably as possible.

I often teach EFT workshops for hundreds of people at a time, and at those events members of the audience tap along with me and whoever is on stage with me for whatever issues or problems that person is dealing with. From time to time, while they are tapping for the on-stage person's physical symptoms or psychological trauma, members of the audience experience their own over-whelming emotions. They may freeze, become agitated, begin to cry, or in other ways display emotional distress. Please note that tapping does not appear to cause this. Rather, the audience members bring these issues with them and they appear to "show up" as natural memories during the therapeutic process.

We always have skilled EFT practitioners standing by, keeping an eye on things. As soon as someone needs help, it's there. Our support staff takes the affected person to a quiet location and taps with them until they recover from whatever memories sent them over the edge.

Whenever someone is experiencing emotional trauma, the best treatment, I'm convinced, is EFT tapping in an emergency. Calming Reminder Phrases delivered in a soothing, supporting tone of voice help bring the person back to the present moment while reducing stress and anxiety.

One of the complications that can accompany PTSD is what psychologists call "dissociation." Dissociation is usually defined as a state of acute mental decompensation in which thoughts, emotions, sensations, and memories are compartmentalized so that there is a lack of connection between things that are usually associated with each other. This produces gaps or discontinuities in conscious awareness. Certain past events and the person's emotional response to those events are simply not integrated into the person's awareness. The symptoms of dissociation include depersonalization, in which the person feels detached from or "not in" his or her body; derealization, in which the world does not seem real but rather phony, far away, or as though it's a movie; dissociative amnesia, in which the person cannot recall important personal information; and identity confusion or identity alteration, in which the person shifts into an alternative personality. Someone experiencing dissociation can know that he or she went through a terrible ordeal but act as though it was nothing special or unusual, suppressing all of the emotions that would normally accompany the experience.

Just as with PTSD, there are many theories about dissociation, its causes, and how best to treat it.

Unlike those in the mental health field, I'm not concerned with labels and diagnoses. When people present the symptoms associated with a psychological condition, I use the same EFT procedures that I do for any other physical or psychological condition. In other words, there is no such thing as one EFT protocol for dissociation and a separate EFT protocol for abreactions or for any other symptom, aspect, or part of Post-Traumatic Stress Disorder.

I would like to emphasize that I do not encourage EFT students to set themselves up as PTSD experts. "Don't go where you don't belong" is one of my mottos. EFT practitioners and coaches should comply with state and local regulations and conduct themselves in a professional manner at all times.

That said, I do believe that EFT is the perfect treatment for Post-Traumatic Stress Disorder in all of its guises and that anyone who masters the basics of EFT and then goes on to master its more advanced techniques should be able to help just about anyone recover from PTSD.

In the following report, Lori Lorenz, who worked with combat veterans at our EFT study in San Francisco last March, gives us the details of an intense case of trauma where "only the pros should tread" (my term). Experienced healing practitioners have all had cases where clients protect themselves by repressing or "not remembering" childhood events that involve torture, maiming, murder, sexual abuse, and other unspeakable atrocities. Sometimes these clients appear to lead a normal life until, eventually, these memories show up and cause severe disorientation.

Lori's sessions with Trish should be very helpful —especially for the pros who deal with this category of clients. Please note her use of the Tearless Trauma

Technique. Also note that a difficult case like this, with many complicating aspects, does not lend itself to being a "one-minute wonder." There is much to unravel here that multiple sessions are typically necessary, sometimes spanning months.

Lori refers in passing to a "forest" of problems. This is a reference to one of my favorite analogies, in which I describe how with EFT, you can cut down a few trees in a forest of traumatic memories, and long before you address them all individually, the whole forest collapses.

For privacy reasons, the actual atrocities are not described and, as with most of the reports in this book, the client's name has been changed.

Where Only the Pros Should Tread

by Lori Lorenz

Trish was referred to me by a caring family member because, despite her outwardly beautiful, active, loving family life, she seemed to be falling apart. Within the past few weeks, terrifying dreams and intrusive waking images from her childhood began appearing out of "nowhere." Even though she knew her childhood was not pleasant and that her family was pretty dysfunctional, these "memories" were outside the realm of anything she thought could actually occur in ANY family, least of all hers. She was terrified of both the "memories" (if they were true) and the possibility that she was "going insane" (if they weren't).

When Trish entered my office, she was barely holding herself together. Within minutes she was relating the extreme content of these new "memories" and entering into gripping states of flashback and immobilizing terror, eyes glazed and unfocused, body shaking.

Even with an established relationship and familiarity with the client's history, most practitioners find such a situation to be pretty unnerving. In the "old days," there was little one could do during this ordeal but provide comfort, keep the person oriented, and introduce some countering thoughts. However, with our EFT tools, we have much more with which to help.

Using a strong voice, I kept reminding Trish where she was and asking her to keep looking into my eyes to help her orient herself. It seemed that a strong and directive voice was needed to help her focus as she moved in and out of being present. I briefly explained EFT as this "weird stuff" of tapping on the meridians to process the emotions and, despite her strong skepticism, she was willing to try, even though she was quite sure nothing could help her.

I often use the TAB (Touch and Breathe) method for EFT, which can be very soothing and introspective. Instead of tapping, you simply hold each acupoint while breathing in and breathing out. But in this case, strong tapping seemed the best way to get her body sensations going in order to counter the body memories and the feeling of being disconnected from her body that seemed to be overwhelming her. So we started tapping on "this emotion," "this terror," and "this overwhelm." At times I had to tap and speak for her when she was immobilized, which I did with her permission. After several rounds of EFT tapping, she was able to achieve some orientation and a sense of calm. I'll never forget the look of disbelief on her face when she sat back, looked at me with clearly present eyes, and said she couldn't believe it but, whatever this stuff was, it was working.

As Trish calmed somewhat, she expressed her greater fear that she was going crazy, that these memories couldn't be true, and that people just didn't do these things to children. I let her know that unfortunately people do, but we didn't have to decide anything about the truth of her images at that point, we just wanted her out of this terror and sense of feeling overwhelmed.

So we started Gary's Tearless Trauma Technique by simply referring to "these memories," "these images," "this terror," and "this confusion" while I frequently reminded her not to go into the memories in detail. She was to intentionally distance herself from them, without dissociating, and just guess at what she might feel if she were to touch into them. I kept reminding her that our intent was not to go into the experience yet, and this helped her discover that she had some control over the intrusiveness of the thoughts as well as the feeling of being overwhelmed.

Once Trish had a sense that she could use EFT to counter the intensity of the memories, she began to describe them. We worked carefully with the details and tapped often whenever the intensity rose. There was little hope of coming down to a zero on any of these far-reaching, many-aspected events, and there was little time to keep track of these zero-to-10 measurements anyway. Nonetheless, we did some general monitoring of the intensity and her sense of whether or not she could handle it. For Trish, at least at that moment, having a place to describe these horrific events seemed more important for her sense of sanity than trying to neutralize a "forest" of unknown extent in a single two-hour session.

By the end of our first session, Trish was absolutely convinced of the efficacy of EFT. She was determined to use it as much as was needed to take back her ability to live her own life while working through whatever was needed to discover the truth and heal it. By our meeting the next day she had used the EFT extensively for the memories and nightmares with impressive relief.

In the past eight months, Trish has discovered the truth of these memories, received several validations from external sources, and has courageously faced layer after layer of experience which would not be believed by most people—even in a horror film or documentary. Her experience of calculated abuse over more than a decade ranks among the most intense I've encountered or read about. And that's saying a lot because my work has included the type of intense trauma that has resulted in Multiple Personality Disorder and severely repressed memories. Through this healing, in which her primary tool has been EFT, Trish has grown and deepened in her capacity to love, experience joy, and connect with her husband and children in ways that amaze her and bring tears to her eyes.

The fact that she has reached this point in only eight months is almost unheard of, even for less extensive mind-controlling abuse than she suffered. At one point in our work, Trish considered having a local therapist work with her in person. I travel to her city only every four to six weeks, and we work by phone between trips.

Trish interviewed five or six professionals who specialize in abuse, each of whom either gave a dismal prognosis and predicted years of painful, traumatizing work to get through the experiences she outlined or simply declined to work with her. Wisely, Trish opted to stay with EFT. She occasionally schedules a session or two when some new aspect or layer of experience surfaces. The rest she handles with EFT using her (by now) excellent skills, and those issues are getting easier to clear, with faster results.

12

EFT for
PTSD's Many Causes

Far from the battlefield, anyone can experience Post-Traumatic Stress Disorder. Although it often follows accidents, illness, physical assaults, and other traumatic events, PTSD's underlying causes can include verbal abuse, acute disappointments, embarrassment, heartache, and even causes that are never discovered.

The same Setup phrases and strategies that work well for military PTSD can be adapted for any kind of trauma, stress, or anxiety. EFT works for people of all ages, including children.

Dealing with Anger

When it comes to recovering from just about any set-back that life has to offer, the emotion that can interfere the most and cause the most damage is anger. Yet even when we understand that, it can be difficult to forgive, forget, and let go. As Dr. Nagy observed, anger is one of our hard-wired emotions. It's easy to get upset, direct anger toward a particular person or institution, or even toward God or Mother Nature, and then stay mad. It's also easy to justify our anger. We may see how destructive anger is when we see it in other people, but our own anger is different. We may even go out of our way to feed anger and keep it alive, believing that to let our guard down and let go of anger or unforgiveness puts us in a vulnerable position, lets the enemy win, or means that we approve of or condone what happened.

In my experience, letting go of anger always pays more dividends than holding onto it. In fact, I consider anger a major impediment to physical and emotional healing. At the same time, I appreciate how tenacious this emotion can be. Intellectually deciding to release anger and actually doing so are two different things.

Yet, in many cases, anger that has lasted for years, even dozens of years, has evaporated in just a few minutes with the help of EFT. The key is correcting the energy disruption that prevents the person from seeing the situation any differently from the way he or she has been seeing it all along. EFT tapping removes the energy blocks that contribute to anger, and as soon as that happens, the person's perspective changes and old grudges don't seem important any more.

Total forgiveness can seem like an impossible homework assignment. Fortunately, the simple strategy of giving up a little anger can go a long way toward releasing the rest. Some ways to do this are to project your release of anger far into the future or to make the whole project indefinite.

...I choose to know that I can some day release this anger...

...I might someday, perhaps, forgive him a little...

This all sounds very vague, but it replaces a flat "it's never going to happen" with the possibility of a future transformation.

Dr. Patricia Carrington encourages people to approach forgiveness by giving up one percent of their anger or unforgiveness. Her "one-percent solution" is a highly effective technique.

"Even though I'm outraged at what he did, I choose to let go of one percent of my anger against him."

"Even though I'm furious about what happened, I choose to release one percent of the rage I feel."

Deciding to give up one percent of a harmful emotion creates a small release that almost always manifests as a large release.

EFT instructor Ann Adams gives us the details (including several sets of Setup language) behind a relatively simple case involving accident flashbacks. This is a common problem and thus Ann's message should help many clients.

Rapid Relief from Accident Flashbacks
by Ann Adams

Last year one of our terrific cooks at our residential program, Brenda, had two traffic accidents in less than six weeks. The irony was that both accidents occurred at the same intersection on her way home from work.

She didn't break any bones but had whiplash and other physical problems. She had weeks of physical therapy and was out of work for four months. She returned to work last August. In November, she shared with me that she was still having flashbacks of the accident and trouble sleeping. Since I was conducting another staff training on using EFT the following week, I suggested she attend.

I started the training session with a brief explanation of the technique and led everyone right into an exercise, explaining that they did not have to believe this exercise would work. I asked them to pick a specific incident in their life that still upset them when they thought about it and then write down their current intensity on a scale of zero to 10.

Then we did three group rounds starting with: *"Even though I have this upset feeling, I deeply and completely accept myself."* After two slow deep breaths, I asked them to think about their upset and write down the number again.

The inevitable surprised looks came on some faces. Several said the upset incident didn't bother them any more. Brenda said, *"Oh my goodness!"* and I asked if she'd like to elaborate on that statement. She was working on the second traffic accident and said, *"I can still see it happen but I am calm now. It is over and I am okay."* I asked for her number and she said it was a zero. She seemed so comfortable talking about it that I asked if she would like to work on other aspects of the accident as a demonstration in front of the group.

She agreed but wanted to remain seated. I asked her to think of the worst part of the accident and she said she was so afraid of being hit again that she drove five extra miles coming and going to work in a detour around the "accident intersection." Her fear of being hit again at that intersection was at least a 9.

We tapped several times for:

Even though I am afraid to drive through the intersection...

Even though I am afraid I will be hit again...

Even though I feel helpless to prevent being hit by a car...

I asked her to picture herself passing that intersection on her way home but to stop at any point she felt herself getting upset again. She began by picturing herself getting in the car, starting it, and then passing each landmark along the way until she got to the intersection where she had the two wrecks.

She closed her eyes and was quiet for a few seconds. Then she said she was still a little apprehensive when she got close enough to actually see the intersection. Her intensity level was a 6. So we tapped twice through the points for: *"Even though I still have some apprehension about getting close to where the accident happened..."*

When asked to take a deep breath and give me a number; she reported it was now a 2. I told the audience that I wanted to show them another step and for those who still had any level of upset to think about their problem and follow along. So Brenda and the audience did the 9 Gamut procedure and another round of tapping. Brenda was smiling now and said she thought she could go home the shorter way.

I suggested to Brenda that she use the remaining time in the staff training to work on any other scenes of the accident that still affected her. And, as always, I gave the group a handout that describes the process and encouraged them to use it for everything.

That was in November. About the middle of January, I had an opportunity to ask Brenda about her feelings now about the accident. She said, *"That stuff you did really helped"* and told me she not only had been able to drive home the shorter way but that after the training she was able to sleep and that she no longer was having flashbacks about the cars ramming into her.

But she said that something about it still bothered her — it was a nagging kind of feeling that something was still wrong. Wrong with what? I asked. *"Wrong with me,"* she said. She was meaning emotionally, so I took a guess and said that sometimes victims felt that in some way they were responsible for what had happened to them. She said, *"Yes, I feel like I should have been able to do something to stop it. That I shouldn't have been driving by that intersection that day."*

We started tapping for:

"Even though I ought to have been able to do something…"

"Even though I feel responsible…"

"Even though I feel guilty for the accident…"

Brenda then laughed and told me that she couldn't see now how she could have thought she was responsible. There was nothing she could have done to stop it. *"It was not my fault."*

I asked her to close her eyes again and pictured both accidents, including the police and hospital experiences, and to stop at any point there was any upset. About a minute passed and she opened her eyes and said no. *"That's amazing."*

❋ ❋ ❋

Rape is another difficult situation, one made worse by the social stigmas associated with it. Our trainings and newsletter archives provide many examples of EFT helping people of all ages overcome the very serious psychological damage caused by rape and sexual molestation.

In this next report, Jeanne Ranger describes how she used EFT to resolve a "date rape" that had caused many years of anguish.

EFT Clears Up a Long-Ago Date Rape Trauma

by Jeanne Ranger

George and I had dated a few times when I was 15. He seemed very loving and tender, always expressing his love for me. No one had ever loved me before. It was quite a new phenomenon for me. I didn't know quite what to make of it, but I liked it.

One night while we sat in his car, he said he loved me and wanted to marry me over and over again. But as he said these things, he was pushing me down against the seat, tugging at my clothes. I struggled against him because this didn't seem right, but as I struggled he forced my head under and behind the steering wheel. My head was almost to the floor and I remember feeling the pedals. Each time I tried to get up my head was stuck and I couldn't get in an upright sitting position. But I didn't scream. I couldn't fight against him. He did his dirty deed. I didn't tell anyone. I never saw him again. I was alone. There was no one to help me. Love had come into my life briefly, and love hurt.

This date rape issue is an incident I thought I had dealt with successfully with talk therapy before EFT. When it came up again a few months back, I tapped it down to level of intensity of 0 out of 10 with EFT. Yet there it was again, alive and squeezing at my heart, screaming for release. So I immediately started tapping:

> *Even though I feel dirty and undeserving…*
>
> *Even though I couldn't scream…*
>
> *Even though I couldn't fight against him…*
>
> *Even though I couldn't scream…*
>
> *Even though I didn't expect that…*

Even though I was so naive to think he really loved me...

Even though I never dreamed that could happen...

Even though I did nothing to stop him...

Even though I feel so guilty...

Even though I couldn't scream...

Even though I feel so ashamed...

Even though I was such a wimp...

Even though I couldn't scream...

Even though I was alone and no one to help me...

Even though I was so naive and didn't know what to do...

Even though I let that young girl tell me how to feel...

Even though I listened to that young girl all this time...

Even though I couldn't scream...

I was stuck on screaming. I somehow had to scream. I was in the bathroom so I turned on the fan, and the water full blast, grabbed some towels put them hard on my face and started to scream, and scream into the towels until I couldn't scream anymore. Then I continued tapping:

Even though I couldn't scream then I can scream now...

Even though I still feel so ashamed...

Even though I was so stupid to think he really loved me...

Even though I still feel so guilty...

Even though I feel so guilty but I know it wasn't my fault...

Even though I let him take advantage of me...

Even though I let that event control much of my adult life...

Even though I'm still alone, it's not in the way that I was alone before...

Even though I have trouble forgiving myself for being such a wimp...

Even though I let that young girl protect me in the only way she knew how, she doesn't' need to protect me anymore... She can stop now... She can rest now... It's time for her to come in... It's time for "us" to unite, to be one... I can protect her now... I choose to protect her now... I choose to love her, and give her what she desires... That little girl that was me and I are together now... I choose to love her and protect her, and take care of her, like she tried her best to do with me... She just didn't know what to do. I know what to do now.

I choose to let go of the guilt and the shame... No more guilt, no more shame... Letting it go... It wasn't my fault... I did not cause it... I choose to forgive myself... I forgive myself... I am willing to look at forgiving George, the bastard; he really took advantage of me.

I was so naive... I knew nothing... I wonder how many others he date-raped like he did me... He knew what he was doing... Maybe that was the only way he could feel good about himself... George is a sick individual... He needs help... He's the wimp... I need to forgive him, so I can let this go once and for all.

George, you bastard, I forgive you... George, I don't want you in my life on any level anymore, so I completely forgive you, and let you go... I forgive myself for hanging on to this for so long... Letting it go... Letting it all go... I am safe, and I am happy... I completely love and accept myself.

At long last, I was free of the date-rape incident. I was able to scream and I feel cleansed. I have also been able to clear several other painful core issues with EFT. I am so grateful to my friend Paul, who sent me the information on EFT. It's taken over my life. I immersed myself in it. I researched it, read about it, ordered all the available material, and studied it at every hour of the day and night. I began to treat myself for physical and emotional ailments, and to bring relief to my friends, their friends, family members, and whoever showed any interest in wanting to try it out. It works! It has become my passion.

❋ ❋ ❋

13

Do-It-Yourself EFT

Can someone who has experienced traumatic events safely learn EFT on his or her own? Can someone who is not a trained psychotherapist or other professional help a friend, spouse, or relative who suffers from PTSD? Is there a danger that the tapping will just open up old wounds and make them worse? Will the person suffer a painful abreaction?

If you have painful memories and PTSD symptoms and you choose to use EFT to help yourself, here are some suggestions for doing so. Remember, however, that professional help may be indicated, and you are urged to seek out such help should difficult intensity arise.

Dr. Carol Look recommends focusing entirely on stress release and physical symptoms. "By starting with bodily symptoms and daily stress," she says, "you can do a lot to help yourself feel more comfortable while relieving discomfort."

In other words, work at first on general stress relief and whatever aches, pains, or other physical symptoms you have. This will give you an opportunity to try EFT, become familiar with the tapping points, get into the rhythm of tapping, and balance your body's energy. This is the most important foundation you can lay for yourself.

Do this by working through EFT's Basic Recipe, which is described in Chapter Two, for at least three general problems. Do the complete procedure, tapping on all the EFT points with appropriate Reminder Phrases. For example:

Even though it's hard for me to relax, I fully and completely accept myself.

Even though my shoulder hurts, I fully and completely accept myself.

Even though I keep having this headache, I fully and completely accept myself.

Even though I have this overall feeling of stress or tension and I can feel it in my back, I fully and completely accept myself.

Does the EFT make a difference? If you feel less stressed and if your physical symptoms improve, which is what I expect will happen, you're learning to use EFT and your body's energy is responding well.

After a day or two of the Basic Recipe for general stress and physical symptoms, which has prepared you for more advanced work, you can start using EFT to defuse or neutralize the emotional intensity you feel toward recent events. This is not the time to tackle intrusive traumatic memories. We're going to start small.

Assuming that this has been an ordinary week with nothing unusual going on, pick out three things that irritated you and focus on them. For example:

Even though I'm annoyed because the contractor didn't finish the repairs, I fully and completely accept myself.

Even though my boss is being impossible, as usual, I fully and completely accept myself.

Even though my kids make way too much noise, I fully and completely accept myself.

Now review Dr. Patricia Carrington's Choices Method, which is described in Chapter Eight, and add a "solution" statement to each of your Setups. For example:

Even though I have this overall stress and I can feel it in my back, I fully and completely accept myself, I forgive my back, which is doing the best it can, and I choose to surprise myself by relaxing and enjoying life while releasing all the stress in my back and letting my back feel flexible and comfortable in every way.

Even though the contractor didn't finish the repairs and I'm really annoyed, I fully and completely accept myself. Even though it's impossible to get good help and there are always delays and it drives me nuts, I accept myself.

Even though this repair business is noisy and messy and behind schedule and a real distraction, I completely accept myself and I choose to be surprised at how easy it is for me to switch my mind from the things that are going wrong to the things that are going right in my life, which is plenty. I choose to focus on the things that really matter, starting right now.

Try other general Setup phrases that deal with overall rather than specific symptoms, such as:

Even though I feel overwhelmed right now, I choose to be surprisingly okay with that.

Even though I don't want to do this tapping business, it's too weird, I choose to take it one step at a time in a way that truly works for me.

Even though I'm disappointed about what happened, I accept myself, and I'm willing to see it differently.

Even though I'm stuck in this anger and don't want to let it go, I'm open to the possibility that it would be nice to feel more peaceful about this.

I strongly recommend that anyone working alone study the examples these talented practitioners have provided and use them as a model when doing EFT. Work through the Basic Recipe several times a day for at least a week on general issues like stress, physical symptoms, and recent annoyances.

Having done that homework, your next assignment is to choose one or two unhappy events from the past, as far back as childhood, but not one that you have trouble talking about. Start with events that aren't very high on the 10-point intensity scale, like a 3 or 4 at most. Write a Setup for the first event using all of the tips and hints you have been studying.

Only after you have done this homework, practiced on general issues, and then practiced being specific with issues that don't cause much discomfort should you tackle more serious memories.

Don't forget the Tearless Trauma Technique. The instant you start to feel emotional intensity, step back and pause while you tap until you feel more relaxed. Whenever you feel uncomfortable, try a general Setup like:

Even though that makes me really uncomfortable, I fully and completely accept myself. Even though I don't feel comfortable thinking about that right now, I accept myself. Even though I don't want to think about those things, I accept and forgive myself and I choose to let this tapping business do its work so that my stress level comes way down and it's easy for me to remember what happened without being upset.

Don't rush, take your time, and when your intensity level falls to a zero and you feel completely at ease, which often happens after tapping through the Basic Recipe once or twice, try moving forward again. If you still feel uncomfortable, no problem. Keep tapping while you say:

Even though I still have some of this uncomfortable feeling, I fully and completely accept myself.

Even though I still feel uneasy about this memory, I accept myself. Even though I don't feel like remembering what happened, I can step back from that event and just keep tapping until I feel relaxed. I choose to put it on the shelf for now, there's no pressure or deadline, and the important thing is that my energy is balanced, so I am okay, I'm safe, I'm at peace.

For even better results, include some of the phrases and recommendations referred to above, which appear throughout this book. Underline or highlight the words that feel right for you and add them to your Setups whenever you do EFT. Write down words or phrases you would like to incorporate in your EFT work.

It is also helpful to record possible Setups in a notebook. For inspiration, peruse the archives of our free newsletter, available at www.EFTUniverse.com. EFT is like any other tool; the more you use it, the better it works, and the more you practice, the easier it is to create effective statements that address core issues and all of their aspects.

* * *

Pat Farrell successfully diagnosed and treated her own PTSD long after the car crash that caused her symptoms. Pat is a good example of someone who experiences a trauma and then manifests occasional PTSD symptoms without realizing why or without realizing what they mean. I suspect that a large number of us have had similar reactions. This do-it-yourself story offers important insights.

Accident Victim Resolves
Her Own PTSD 40 Years Later

by Pat Farrell

Three times over a period of about 25 years, I experienced shortness of breath, blood draining from my face, and heart palpitations so severe that I had to pull over while driving. Even though this occurred so seldom, these are typical symptoms of PTSD. Eventually, I started putting things together and realized that at each occurrence, I was passing an accident just at the moment that a person on a gurney was being put into an ambulance. By this time I was experienced in EFT and started looking for an explanation.

When I was twenty, which was 40 years ago, I was trapped in a car for three hours while the rescue team tried to extract me after a horrible accident. Four of us in my little car were hit head-on by a 1959 Oldsmobile. That's similar to a tank running over an ant. I realized that during that time, in an unconscious or semi-conscious state, I must have seen or heard the rescuers talking about my friend, Rita.

It wasn't until about a week after the accident, when my family was sure that I would be okay, that they finally told me of Rita's death. While I felt shocked, I remember not really being surprised, and I realized that my subconscious was already aware of the tragedy.

Now, all these years later, I focused on the accident and used EFT to tap on:

Even though I have this stressful response each time I see a body being removed from a car…

Even though the emergency team's removal of Rita's body from the crash is deeply embedded in my subconscious…

Even though I feel responsible for Rita's death…

I tapped on the body points using wording like:

This reaction to bodies being put in an ambulance.

This reaction.

That can't be Rita on the stretcher.

I'm afraid they'll never get me out of the car.

I then used a round of:

I choose to release this subconscious reaction to seeing an accident.

I choose to release this reaction.

Then I did an entire round on guilt about Rita's death and the medical struggles that my friends and fellow passengers Frankie and Danny experienced over the years.

Even though the State Police said it wasn't my fault, I have been holding on to this guilt for forty years…

Even though I didn't feel that people blamed me, I have been holding on to this guilt…

Even though I didn't realize it, I have been punishing myself for all these years...

This guilt that it must have been my fault.

I choose to release this guilt.

I have done lots of work to release the guilt over the years and finally feel free of it thanks to EFT. EFT is truly the miracle drug—without being a drug. I would love to see more use of EFT for Post-Traumatic Stress Disorder.

❀ ❀ ❀

This report by EFT do-it-yourselfer Lisa Rogers should be passed around the planet. It is a major testimony to persistence and points to the limitless possibilities within EFT.

How I Handled
My Child Abuse PTSD All by Myself

by Lisa Rogers

I am not a therapist., and I have no training in the mental health field. In fact, I barely graduated from high school. I am just an ordinary person who had an extraordinary problem. I suffered from Post-Traumatic Stress Disorder.

From age 12, I visited dozens of therapists trying to get help for my depression and anxiety. Years of counseling and prescribed drugs left me frustrated and no closer to relief. My frustration led me to use street drugs and alcohol in an effort to medicate myself.

272 EFT for PTSD

When I found EFT, I had no idea then how much it would change my life. It seemed too good to be true. Nothing else had worked, but since this was something I could do on my own, I decided to give it a try. What did I have to lose? I tapped every day. My ritual was that I would tap every time I went to the bathroom. It was private and I knew I'd be there a few times day!

Although there were many major issues I needed to address, I thought it would be helpful to focus on one at a time. I guess the best place to start is the beginning, with child sexual abuse.

When I was a child, I was severely abused—emotionally, physically and sexually—by a family member. The sexual abuse began when I was eight and continued for four years on a regular basis. When I told my mother, she didn't believe me. This left me with a lasting feeling of shame and guilt that somehow I had done something to cause this. My family treated me like a traitor. I felt like a freak. I ran away from home at 12 and lived on the streets for years. I was an intravenous drug user by 14 and pregnant with my first child at 15.

As the years went by my life was a wreck. I felt alone and misunderstood. I thought I was a bad person. I hated myself and resented the world.

I was suicidal and desperate for help when I found EFT. I ordered the free EFT manual and learned the process. I was afraid to dig too deep, so at first I tapped on my physical feelings only.

Even though I feel like a deer in the headlights...

Even though my heart is pounding out of my chest...

Even though I feel like someone just jumped out and scared me...

Even though I can't concentrate...

Even though the noise hurts me...

Even though the light hurts me...

Even though I'm so nervous for no reason...

Even though I'm terrified and I'm only watching TV...

Even though I keep having these night terrors...

After about a month of tapping every day on my outward symptoms, I could see that EFT really worked. I then felt confident and safe enough to start tapping on specific painful negative emotions.

Even though I hate myself...

Even though I'm trash...

Even though I'm worth nothing...

Even though I deserved it...

Even though I didn't deserve it...

Even though no child ever deserves it...

Even though my parents didn't love me...

Even though my parents didn't protect me...

Even though I should have never told...

Even though I should have told earlier but I was too scared...

Even though I told and it ruined my family and my life...

Even though I can't forget...

Even though these memories won't go away...

Even though it's been years and it still hurts so much...

Even though I feel shame and guilt...

Even though I feel different...

Even though a part of me still thinks it's my fault...

Even though I know it wasn't my fault...

Even though my mom didn't believe me...

Even though everyone thought I was a liar...

Even though it made me hate my body...

Even though child services knew and they didn't protect me...

Even though my mother knew and still won't admit it...

Even though I'll never be normal...

I just kept tapping on whatever came into my head. I would write things down to tap on later if I couldn't tap right then. I was determined. I tapped for another six months on a regular basis. I always checked my progress with the zero-to-10 scale.

I have to note that for the first few months I never tapped on specific abuse memories because they were too painful. I didn't want to relive them so I simply tapped on my feelings surrounding the abuse as a whole. Once I got rid of the guilt and shame I had felt for so long, it was easier to address specific memories because I knew logically that it wasn't my fault. I have since learned to use the Tearless Trauma Technique, where you can imagine thinking about the problem without actually thinking about it. This is a great tool that I use often.

Within a year of finding EFT, my life completely changed. For over five years now I have been clean from drugs and alcohol and have not had a single panic attack. I now love my life and myself. EFT gave me the freedom to be a valuable and productive human being. My personal success with EFT inspired me to help others. I am now an EFT practitioner, helping people to overcome their issues with the Emotional Freedom Techniques.

* * *

Consider next this "impossible" case.

Paramedic Cures His Own PTSD

by Bob Patefield

Two and a half years ago my 14-year career as a Paramedic ended following a diagnosis of Post Traumatic Stress Disorder (PTSD). I was in a real mess with nightmares, flashbacks, intrusive thoughts, and compulsive behaviors, to name a few.

As I traveled around, I would pass places where I had attended serious road accidents and other traumatic events, and they would vividly replay in my mind. I would see the accident in any situation. If someone simply crossed the road in front of me, I would see them fall and injure themselves in graphic detail. I would see my partner off to work in the morning and then was unable get images of her in a serious road accident out of my mind. It was a very unpleasant time.

I'm not sure how I got in this state. It seemed very gradual, although there were some very traumatic incidents in my career. The worst was the attempted murder of two young boys by their father. My colleague on that day never worked again, it was so distressing for him. I managed another seven years. If only I had known about EFT then.

Although I got some basic counseling through my General Practitioner, I was left on a very long waiting list to see a psychologist. I was desperate to find a self-help tool.

I had seen EFT demonstrated two years before, but I wasn't convinced, so when my partner had her longstanding fear of heights diffused very rapidly, I had to look in more detail.

I downloaded the manual and got tapping straight away. I was getting results almost immediately. I would spend an hour or so a day tapping on whatever issues came to mind, shifting here and there, tree to tree, using it to diffuse anxiety and stress in whatever situation arose. I ordered all the EFT materials and used them over the next 12 months, practicing the techniques I learned on myself and others.

When I finally got my appointment to see the psychologist (after a two-year wait) she could find no traces of PTSD at all. She seemed very surprised that I had managed to deal with the PTSD myself, so I told her how I had gone about it. She seemed to think that EFT had somehow suppressed the traumatic feelings and they would resurface in the future. We know different, though.

EFT has helped me not only get over the PTSD, it has also helped me rid myself of tons of negative baggage and self-limiting beliefs from my childhood. I built a growing hi-fi business and set myself up as an EFT Practitioner in Lancashire.

My whole family has benefited from these great techniques, and EFT has made us closer than we have ever been. I am currently offering a free group session to Ambulance staff from my old service, not just for their benefit, but for the benefit of their patients too. There are so many opportunities to use EFT in frontline emergency care that I almost miss being a Paramedic — Mmmm! Night shifts. No. I changed my mind. I don't miss it at all.

❊ ❊ ❊

EFT Glossary

The following terms have specific meanings in EFT. They are referred to in some of the reports included here and are often mentioned in EFT reports.

Acupoints. Acupuncture points which are sensitive points along the body's meridians. Acupoints can be stimulated by acupuncture needles or, in acupressure, by massage or tapping. EFT is an acupressure tapping technique.

Art of Delivery. The sophisticated presentation of EFT that uses imagination, intuition, and humor to quickly discover and treat the underlying causes of pain and other problems. The art of delivery goes far beyond Mechanical EFT.

Aspects are "issues within issues," different facets or pieces of a problem that are related but separate. When new aspects appear, EFT can seem to stop working. In truth, the original EFT treatment continues to work while the new aspect triggers a new set of symptoms. In some cases, many aspects of a situation or problem each require their own EFT treatment. In others, only a few do.

Basic Formula. See Mechanical EFT.

Basic Recipe. A four-step treatment consisting of Setup phrase, Sequence (tapping on acupoints in order), 9-Gamut Treatment, and Sequence. This was the original EFT protocol.

Borrowing Benefits. When you tap with or on behalf of another person, your own situation improves, even though you aren't tapping for your own situation. This happens in one-on-one sessions, in groups, and when you perform surrogate or proxy tapping. The more you tap for others, the more your own life improves.

Chasing the Pain. After applying EFT, physical discomforts can move to other locations and/or change in intensity or quality. A headache described as a sharp pain behind the eyes at an intensity of 8 might shift to dull throb in back of the head at an intensity of 7 (or 9, or 3 or any other intensity level). Moving pain is an indication that EFT is working. Keep "chasing the pain" with EFT and it will usually go to zero or some low number. In the process, emotional issues behind the discomforts are often successfully treated.

Chi. *Chi,* or energy, flows through and around every living being. It is said to regulate spiritual, emotional, mental, and physical balance and to be influenced by *yin* (the receptive, feminine force) and *yang* (the active masculine force). These forces, which are complementary opposites, are in constant motion. When *yin* and *yang* are balanced, they work together with the natural flow of *chi* to help the body achieve and maintain health. *Chi* moves through the body along invisible pathways, or channels, called meridians. Traditional Chinese Medicine identifies 20 meridians along which chi or vital energy flows or circulates through to all parts of the body. Acupoints along the meridians can be stimulated to improve the flow of *Chi* and, in EFT, to resolve emotional issues.

Choices Method. Dr. Patricia Carrington's method for inserting positive statements and solutions into Setup and Reminder Phrases.

Core Issues. Core issues are deep, important underlying emotional imbalances, usually created in response to traumatic events. A core issue is truly the crux of the problem, its root or heart. Core issues are not always obvious but careful detective work can often uncover them, and once discovered, they can be broken down into specific events and handled routinely with EFT.

Generalization Effect. When related issues are neutralized with EFT, they often take with them issues that are related in the person's mind. In this way, several issues can be resolved even though only one is directly treated.

Global. While the term "global" usually refers to something that is universal or experienced worldwide, In EFT it refers to problems, especially in Setup phrases, that are vague and not specific.

Intensity Meter. The zero-to-10 scale that measures pain, discomfort, anger, frustration, and every other physical or emotional symptom. Intensity can also be indicated with gestures, such as hands held close together (small discomfort) or wide apart (large discomfort).

Mechanical EFT. EFT's Basic Formula consists of tapping on the Karate Chop point or Sore Spot while saying three times, "Even though I have this __[problem]__, I fully and complete accept myself" (Setup phrase), followed by tapping the Sequence of EFT acupoints in order, with an appropriate Reminder Phrase.

Meridians. Invisible channels or pathways through which energy or *Chi* flows in the body. The eight primary meridians pass through five pairs of vital organs, and twelve secondary meridians network to the extremities. The basic premise of EFT is that the cause of every negative emotion and most physical symptoms is a block or disruption in the flow of *Chi*, or energy, along one or more of the meridians.

Movie Technique, or Watch a Movie Technique. In this process you review in your mind, as though it were a movie, a bothersome specific event. When intensity comes up, stop and tap on that intensity. When the intensity subsides, continue in your mind with the story. This method has been a mainstay in the tool box of many EFT practitioners. It may be the most-often used EFT technique of all. For a full description, see www.EFTUniverse.com/tutorial/tutorcthree.htm

Personal Peace Procedure. An exercise in which you clear problems and release core issues by writing down, as quickly as possible, as many bothersome events from your life that you can remember. Try for at least 50 or 100. Give each event a title, as though it is a book or movie. When the list is complete, begin tapping on the largest issues. Eliminating at least one uncomfortable memory per day (a very conservative schedule) removes at least 90 unhappy events in three months. If you work through two or three per day, it's 180 or 270. For details, see www.EFTUniverse.com/tutorial/tutormthirteen.htm.

Reminder Phrase. A word, phrase, or sentence that helps the mind focus on the problem being treated. It is used in combination with acupoint tapping.

Setup phrase, or Setup. An opening statement said at the beginning of each EFT treatment which defines and helps neutralize the problem. In EFT, the standard Setup phrase is, "Even though I have this _____, I fully and completely accept myself."

Story Technique, or Tell a Story Technique. Narrate or tell the story out loud of a specific event dealing with trauma, grief, anger, etc., and stop to tap whenever the story becomes emotionally intense. Each of the stopping points represents another aspect of the issue that, on occasion, will take you to even deeper issues. This technique is identical to the Movie Technique except that in the Movie Technique, you simply watch past events unfold in your mind. In the Tell a Story Technique, you describe them out loud.

Surrogate or Proxy Tapping involves tapping on yourself on behalf of another person. The person can be present or not. Another way to perform surrogate or proxy tapping is to substitute a photograph, picture, or line drawing for the person and tap on that.

Tail-enders. The "yes, but" statements that create negative self-talk. When you state a goal or affirmation, tail-enders point the way to core issues.

Tearless Trauma Technique. This is another way of approaching an emotional problem in a gentle way. It involves having the client guess as to the emotional intensity of a past event rather than painfully re-live it mentally.

Writings on Your Walls. Limiting beliefs and attitudes that result from cultural conditioning or family attitudes, these are often illogical and harmful yet very strong subconscious influences.

Yin and Yang. See *Chi,* above.

Index